GW00494961

# WEATHER FORECASTS

Published by the Royal Yachting Association
RYA House, Romsey Road, Eastleigh
Hampshire SO50 9YA
Tel: 0703 629962

# CONTENTS

# 1. YOUR WEATHER FORECAST

Whether sailing, cruising or merely pottering about close inshore there is nothing more important than the weather. Careful attention to the weather forecast can make all the difference between an enjoyable cruise and an expensive salvage claim, between winning and losing a race, between a fast exhilarating beat across the Channel and a long and tedious one, and between a relaxing afternoon afloat and the depressing moans of a wet, bedraggled and half-frozen crew.

You cannot have too much weather information. It is just as important to follow the weather as it is to know the tides, and intelligent following of the weather and the weather forecasts can increase enormously one's interest and enjoyment in a cruise or an afternoon's sailing.

Merely listening to a weather forecast is not enough. Listening habits are such that most people use only half an ear and do not remember the details of the forecast. It is essential to write it down on a note-pad, or better still, on one of the specially designed forms which are available for use with the BBC Shipping Forecast. The majority of weather bulletins are transmitted at normal reading speed, but even so, using a prepared form and simple abbreviations all the information can be taken down. Having got it on paper you can think about it at your leisure and plan your day to make the best possible use of the winds and weather which are expected. You cannot of course listen until you have switched on the radio, and it is surprisingly easy to forget or to be distracted just before a broadcast is due; so set an alarm clock to make sure you do not miss it.

This booklet gives basic guidance on the content and terminology of weather forecasts to enable yachtsmen to understand and collate the information which is given. It also contains details of telephone and fax marine weather services in Britain and France, and weather broadcasts for British home waters and for most of the coastal areas around western Europe including the western Mediterranean. These details are liable to change but it is hoped that most will remain valid until the next edition is produced.

A more comprehensive and detailed discussion of the weather as it affects sailors is to be found in *Weather at Sea: a Yachtmaster's Guide*, Second Edition 1991, by David Houghton published by Fernhurst Books.


## 1. Times and frequencies

Weather bulletins broadcast by national radio services such as the BBC may be picked up on most portable radio receivers. In addition there is a large number of coastal radio stations giving weather bulletins several times a day at fixed times, each for a limited number of sea areas local to the station and together covering all sea areas around the coasts of western Europe. These coast radio station bulletins are broadcast on the VHF (156-174 MHz) and MF (1500-3,500 kHz) maritime bands and may be received on all marine radio-telephone equipment and also on some portable receivers.

Since Admiralty Notices to Mariners, the Admiralty list of Radio Signals and the World Meteorological Organisation Publications show times in GMT, the tables in Chapter 8 give times of broadcast also in GMT. You will often have to add 1 or 2 hours to the times shown when planning to pick up broadcasts.

Frequencies shown as kHz may be converted into metres by doing the simple sum in Section 7 of Chapter 8. A formula for conversion from metres per second is also given. A few countries use these units for wind speed instead of knots.

## 2. Warning services

Gale warnings form an important part of the weather services provided by national and coastal radio stations and via Navtex. Always remember however that warnings are issued mostly for winds of gale force (34 knots) and above because at this strength the wind becomes a hazard for commercial shipping and trawling. The 'yachtsman's gale' is more like Force 6 (22 to 27 knots) while for many small sailing and motor boats Force 4 (11 to 16 knots) is the limit of safety.

A warning service operates for the benefit of small craft in coastal waters of Britain. Warnings are sent by the Regional Weather Centre to the local radio station serving the area affected whenever the wind is expected to increase to force 6 or more within the following 12 hours on the coast or within 5 miles seaward. The warnings are broadcast in the first programme break following receipt of the message and repeated on the following hour after the news bulletin. Most local BBC and Independent radio stations with coverage of coastal areas co-operate in this service which operates from Easter through to the end of October.

Warnings of strong (force 6 or 7) coastal winds are also issued by the Met Office Weather Centres to HM Coastguard whenever such winds are expected within the next 12 hours up to 5 miles from the coast and there is no gale warning in operation for the sea area concerned. They are broadcast on receipt throughout the year on Channel 67 preceded by announcement on Channel 16.

## 3. Special forecast services

Clubs may, for a small fee, make arrangements with their nearest Met Office Weather Centre for the provision of special forecasts and warnings for particular sailing events. Weather charts sent by telephone facsimile can be a very useful part of such a service. A list of Weather Centres and their telephone and fax numbers is given in Chapter 8, section 3.

For long offshore passages weather routeing services are available from the Met Office or Noble Denton - see Chapter 8 section 3.

## 4. New service - GMDSS - INMARSAT - C

The Global Maritime Distress and Safety System (GMDSS), of which NAVTEX is an integral part, will provide for the worldwide automatic receipt on board of navigational and weather information in English transmitted by satellite (Inmarsat) via Standard-C. GMDSS also encompasses radiotelex and telephony broadcasts for coastal waters. It is already operational in the North Atlantic/European sector (METAREAS 1, 2 and 3). Warnings and forecasts for METAREA 1, the northeast Atlantic north of 48N and provided by Bracknell are broadcast from the BT Inmarsat station at Goonhilly. METAREA 2 covering the northeast Atlantic south of 48N, and METAREA 3, the Mediterranean, are the responsibility of the French Met Service. The times of the main weather bulletins, all of them in English, for the areas are:-

METAREA 1 – 0930 and 2030 GMT
METAREA 2 – 0900 and 2100 GMT
METAREA 3 – 1015 GMT

## 2. FORECASTS ON UK RADIO, TELEVISION AND TELECOM

All weather forecasts broadcast by the BBC are prepared either in the Met Office's Central Forecast Office at Bracknell or in one of its Weather Centres. All shipping forecasts read by the BBC announcer are written in the Central Forecast Office and sent by Telex to the BBC. All forecasts broadcast by Coast Radio Stations originate from the Central Forecast Office, as do all gale warnings for sea areas.

## 1. Shipping forecasts

Shipping forecasts are broadcast on Radio 4 (1515 metres, 198 kHz and FM) at 0033, 0555, 1355, 1750, daily. These are clock times.

Gale warnings are part of the shipping forecast service and are broadcast at the earliest juncture in the Radio 4 programme after receipt from the Met Office, and also after the next following news bulletin.

Each Shipping Forecast Bulletin comprises three parts:

### General synopsis
This is very important because it gives the information you need to estimate the time of occurrence of any changes which are forecast for individual sea areas. It tells you about depressions, anticyclones, troughs and fronts which will control the winds and weather over the sea areas in the forecast period. It tells you where they were just before the broadcast was written, which way they are moving and where they are expected to be at the end of the forecast period. Careful interpolation on the basis of the General Synopsis will often double the amount of information you can get from the sea area forecast which follows. The meanings of terms which are used are given in Chapter 4, Section 6.

### Sea area forecast
For each sea area or group of areas around the British Isles a forecast is given of wind, weather and visibility for the following 24 hours. The areas are given in fixed sequence and to save time the words "wind", "force", "weather", "visibility" are omitted. The meanings of the terms used are given in Chapter 4.

### Reports from coastal stations
All the bulletins end with a list of weather reports from coastal stations around the British Isles. These give the reported wind direction and force, significant weather if any (if the weather is fair or fine nothing is said), visibility in miles or metres, barometric pressure in millibars and the barometric tendency (i.e., whether rising, falling or steady). These reports are very useful because not only do they tell you what the weather is nearest to you but they give you enough detail with the general synopsis to enable you to construct your own weather map. Do not forget though, when you are drawing your weather map, the coastal reports are always for a later time than the 'main chart time' (0001, 0600, 1200, 1800 GMT) for which the positions of depressions, troughs etc. are given in the general synopsis. If you are constructing your own weather map, and you should do it for the time of the coastal station reports, you will need to move on the troughs, and fronts, etc., and adjust the positions given in the general synopsis to the time of the coastal reports, using the speeds given in the general synopsis.

Increasingly manned weather reporting stations are being replaced by automatic ones, and it is important to be aware of their limitations. Automatic stations are not yet capable of reporting 'weather', ie whether it is raining, snowing etc; or of measuring visibility in excess of 5 miles. So if the visibility is reported as 5 miles, it

6

does not necessarily mean that it is only 5 miles. Even more importantly, if the visibility is reported as, say, 500 metres, you have to judge whether the low value is due to fog, rain or snow.

## 2. Inshore waters forecasts

Forecasts for inshore waters (up to 12 miles offshore) around Britain are broadcast twice daily. The morning forecast can be heard on BBC Radio 3 (90.2-92.4 FM) at 0655 clock time. The late night forecast is broadcast just before close down, normally following the Shipping Forecast, on BBC Radio 4 (198 kHz, 1515m and FM). The Radio 4 bulletin includes the most recent available actual weather reports from a selection of coastal stations whose location is given in Section 2 of Chapter 8. Details of the precise times of broadcast are published in Radio Times.

## 3. Land area forecasts

These are important because:
(a) They include an outlook which is usually for two days beyond the period of the detailed forecast and the shipping forecast. On a fairly recent occasion stormy weather was predicted in the weekend outlook at the end of a Friday lunchtime forecast. This was not mentioned in the shipping forecast since the change was not due until well after the end of the period covered by the shipping forecast, but sailors who took action on the land area forecast saved themselves a lot of trouble and inconvenience, while some who did not heed the forecasts were shipwrecked and taken ashore by the rescue services.
(b) They may give details about coastal weather for which there is not space in the shipping bulletin.

## 4. Forecasts and reports on local radio

All local radio stations near the coast broadcast weather forecasts for the local area and many of them include information on winds and weather over the nearby coastal waters, particularly during the summer months. Since the time and content of the various broadcasts are frequently adjusted the detailed information is not included in this booklet. However, you will find that the best times to tune into your local radio station for a weather bulletin are between 30 and 35 minutes past 6, 7 and 8 o'clock, and/or sometime between 0650 and 0715, and again between 0750 and 0815, and between 1700 and 1830.

## 5. Forecasts and reports by telephone and fax

Forecasts and up-to-date weather reports are readily available by both telephone and telephone fax for all coasts, coastal and inland waters of the UK. The high quality services are provided by the Met Office in co-operation with Telephone Information Services Ltd. The call charge is at the premium rate of 49p per minute standard rate, and 39p per minute at all other times. This charge is the same irrespective of distance.

The *Marinecall* and *MetFAX Marine* services are specially designed for sailors and fishermen.

fishermen.
The *Marinecall* (telephone) service provides on separate numbers:

- 2-day forecasts for coastal waters of the UK in 15 separate areas. Each forecast comprises any gale and strong wind warnings in force, a general synopsis, a forecast of wind, weather, visibility, air temperature, sea state and sea temperature for the next 24 hours and an outlook for the following 24 hours.
- The latest available hourly weather reports for stations in each area.
- 3 to 5-day planning forecasts. Currently four areas are covered; viz. UK, English Channel, Southern North Sea, and Irish Sea. More will probably be added in April/May 1994, including the Channel Islands, Southwest Approaches, Biscay and Finisterre.

The *MetFAX Marine* service (the first two items below are also known as *Marinecall Fax*) provides on separate numbers;

- 2-day forecasts for all coastal waters of the UK in 15 separate areas – as provided on the *Marinecall* telephone service – plus the latest actual and forecast (24-hour) weather maps.
- 3 to 5-day planning forecasts for each of the four areas, UK, English Channel, Southern North Sea and Irish Sea – plus the latest forecast weather maps for 2 and 3 days ahead. More areas will probably be added in April/May 1994, including the Channel Islands, Southwest Approaches, Biscay and Finisterre.
- the latest actual and forecast weather maps (without written forecasts attached).
- a chart of the latest weather reports from some 60 stations over the British Isles and adjacent European coasts. The reports are plotted in standard format - a key is included - giving details of wind, pressure, temperature, cloud and weather. The chart can be accessed approximately 30 minutes after the time of the reports and is updated every three hours. You can easily use it to construct your own weather map, drawing the isobars from the pressure readings, and so follow weather changes throughout the day in considerable detail.
- the latest shipping forecast as broadcast on Radio 4.
- 2 to 5-day planning forecasts for Northwest Scottish and Northern North Sea shipping areas.
- the latest picture from the weather satellite.

*Weathercall* is essentially a landsman's forecast, but you will need it for sailing on inland waters.

A list of products available on *Marinecall*, *MetFAX Marine* and *Weathercall* and telephone numbers at the time of going to press is in Chapter 8 section 3. It includes update times. New items are expected to be added in April/May 1994, and an up-to-date menu of fax products can be obtained by dialling the Index page
Similar fax services are provided for pilots, – *MetFAX Aviation* – and schools – *MetFAX Education* – and you may find some of these products of interest. For instance the *MetFAX Education* menu includes plotted weather reports for the east coast of the USA. Dialling codes for all the index pages will be found in Chapter 8 Section 3.

## 6. Forecasts via the Coastguard

Coastguard Marine Rescue Co-ordination Centres (MRCCs) and Sub-Centres (MRSCs) (listed in Chapter 8, Section 4) broadcast Met Office local inshore waters forecasts every 4 hours and any gale or strong wind warnings in force every 2 hours. Actual weather reports may also be included. The broadcasts are on Channel 67 after announcement on Channel 16.

## 7. Forecast for North Sea fishing

A 3-day forecast of winds for the North Sea fishing fleet provided by Aberdeen Weather Centre is broadcast daily on 2226 kHz from October to March. The forecast for sea areas Fair Isle, Viking, Forties and Fisher is broadcast at 0820 and 2020; and for Tyne, Dogger, German Bight, Humber, Thames at 0945 and 2145.

## 8. Television and teletext weather forecasts

Most BBC and ITV channels give regular coverage around news times and near close down. The chart shown is usually the latest actual chart, but in some of the longer presentations a forecast chart is also included. Both Ceefax and Oracle services include weather information and forecasts.

## 9. Navtex and radio-facsimile and Volmet

**Navtex**
Navtex is an international navigational telex service broadcasting safety related messages in English on 518 kHz. Dedicated receiving equipment is readily available and not expensive. The simplest version comprises a receiver tuned to the frequency, a small printer and a chip which controls what is received and printed. All messages are prefixed by a 4-character 'word'. The first character identifies the transmitting station, the second the category of message and the remainder are two serial numbers. Details will be found in Chapter 8, Section 6. This facility to receive gale warnings and marine weather forecasts automatically is particularly valuable for anyone cruising offshore.

**Radio-facsimile**
Weather maps, both actual and forecast, and pictures from weather satellites are broadcast according to fixed schedules by a number of national meteorological services. Some of the 'actual' weather charts also include weather observations from selected meteorological stations presented in the standard international code. They are intended mainly for professional use, but they will benefit anyone able to read a weather map. Information on the most useful fax broadcasts is in Chapter 8, Section 5.

**Volmet**
Volmet is a meteorological service for aviators available on HF (SSB mode), and on VHF in southern England and parts of Scotland. It is a continuous broadcast of airfield weather reports and short period forecasts. Sailors keenly interested in the weather will find the information interesting and in some instances useful. Details of frequencies are given in Chapter 8, Section 7.

9

Shipping bulletins are broadcast at normal reading speed so it is necessary to have a prepared form with at least all the sea areas listed and some form of shorthand notation for the majority of the standard words and phrases. Pads of forms suitable for recording shipping forecasts are available from the RYA and most Weather Centres. There is nothing to stop you devising your own shorthand so long as you can remember afterwards the meaning of what you have written, but there is a lot to be said for using a notation which has been evolved by those with considerable experience in using shipping bulletins and which includes a number of the standard international weather map symbols. Once you are familiar with the more common of these international symbols you will be able to appreciate at a glance the information on any weather map which you may see displayed in clubs or at ports of call.

### The general synopsis

Few international symbols are involved here except of course for the points of the compass – N, S, NW, SW, etc – but it is not possible to write down the synopsis until you have practised a simple shorthand using initial letters for terms such as depression, anticyclone, low, high, warm front, cold front, occlusion, trough, ridge etc., and for the various sea areas which are usually referred to in giving the positions of the weather systems. One very useful hint is to use an oblique stroke to denote the passage of time, and this applies particularly to the sea area forecasts as we shall see. Also it is often a good idea to denote movement by an arrow.

### The sea area forecast

**Wind** – The simplest forecast is in the form 'northwest 5', which is obviously abbreviated as 'NW 5'. Often however we have something like 'northwest 4 to 5 at first, backing southwest and increasing to 7 to gale 8 by end of the period' which should be written as 'NW 4–5/SW 7–8', and all the rest of the words can be inferred from this simple shorthand form. Note particularly the use of an oblique stroke to distinguish between 'at first' and 'later'. 'In the South at first' abbreviates to 'In S/' whereas 'In the South later' would abbreviate to '/in S'. The words 'temporarily', 'occasionally', 'locally' are often used and should be abbreviated to 'tem', 'occ', 'loc'.
**Weather** – This is always given in terms such as 'fair', 'showers', 'rain' etc. Here international shorthand should be used and you can choose between the Beaufort letter notation or the international weather map symbols as given below. There is something to be said for using the international map symbols because you can then plot these directly onto your map, but the former are much easier to learn and you can readily turn them into plotting symbols at your leisure after the broadcast. The phrases 'at first', 'later' are often used and, again, an oblique stroke comes in very useful. For instance 'rain at first, showers later' can be abbreviated to 'r/p'. This sort of detail should always be taken down as it almost certainly ties in with a change of wind and the passage of an important weather system through the sea area.

## Abridged Beaufort weather notation and international plotting symbols

| Beaufort letter | | Plotting symbol |
|---|---|---|
| r | rain | ● |
| d | drizzle | 🌢 |
| s | snow | ✳ |
| p | shower | ▽ |
| h | hail | △ |
| th | thunderstorm | ⊼ |
| q | squall | ⩔ |
| m | mist | = |
| f | fog | ≡ |
| z | haze | ∞ |

For heavy precipitation, capital letters are used e.g. R – heavy rain.

**Visibility** – A straightforward abbreviation of 'g' for 'good', 'm' for 'moderate', 'p' for 'poor' is all that is required here, remembering again to use a vertical stroke to denote a passage of time and also to take down all the details which are given about fog. Fog will be discussed in more detail later under the discussion on weather hazards in Chapter 7.

## Coastal station reports

As with the sea area forecasts you need a prepared form with the coastal stations already listed, and columns for the reports which are always given for each station in the sequence wind, significant weather (fair and fine are not 'significant' and are not mentioned – if nothing is said about the weather you should assume that it is fair or fine), visibility in miles or metres, barometric pressure in millibars, and finally pressure tendency (i.e. whether the barometer is rising or falling, and how rapidly, or whether it is steady). The same shorthand should be used as for the sea area forecasts. There is no need to write down the words miles or metres as one or two figures will always be miles and three or four figures will always be metres. The pressure tendency should be abbreviated to s for steady, r for rising, rs for rising slowly, etc: or you can use a stroke inclined at various angles according to the way you would observe the pressure tendency on a barograph. The definitions of the terms used for pressure tendency are given on page 15.

## BEAUFORT SCALE OF WIND FORCE

| Beaufort No. | General Description | Sea Criterion | Landsman's Criterion | Limits of velocity in Knots |
|---|---|---|---|---|
| 0 | Calm | Sea like a mirror | Calm; smoke rises vertically. | Less than 1 |
| 1 | Light air | Ripples with the appearance of scales are formed, but without foam crests. | Direction of wind shown by smoke drift but not by wind vanes. | 1 to 3 |

11

| | | | | |
|---|---|---|---|---|
| 2 | Light breeze | Small wavelets, still short but more pronounced. Crests have a glassy appearance and do not break. | Wind felt on face; leaves rustle; ordinary vane moved by wind. | 4 to 6 |
| 3 | Gentle breeze | Large wavelets. Crests begin to break. Foam of glassy appearance. Perhaps scattered white horses. | Leaves and small twigs in constant motion. Wind extends light flags. | 7 to 10 |
| 4 | Moderate breeze | Small waves becoming longer, fairly frequent white horses. | Raises dust and loose paper; small branches are moved. | 11 to 16 |
| 5 | Fresh breeze | Moderate waves, taking more pronounced long form; many white horses are formed. Chance of some spray. | Small trees in leaf begin to sway. Crested wavelets form on inland waters. | 17 to 21 |
| 6 | Strong breeze | Large waves begin to form; the white foam crests are more extensive everywhere. Probably some spray. | Large branches in motion; whistling heard in telegraph wires, umbrellas used with difficulty. | 22 to 27 |
| 7 | Near gale | Sea heaps up and white foam from breaking waves begins to be blown in streaks along the direction of the wind. | Whole trees in motion; inconvenience felt when walking against wind. | 28 to 33 |
| 8 | Gale | Moderately high waves of greater length; edges of crests begin to break into spindrift. The foam is blown in well-marked streaks along the direction of the wind. | Breaks twigs off trees; generally impedes progress. | 34 to 40 |
| 9 | Severe gale | High waves. Dense streaks of foam along the direction of the wind. Crests of waves begin to topple, tumble and roll over. Spray may affect visibility. | Slight structural damage occurs (chimney-pots and slates removed). | 41 to 47 |
| 10 | Storm | Very high waves with long overhanging crests. The resulting foam in great patches is blown in dense white streaks along the direction of the wind. On the whole the surface takes on a white appearance. The tumbling of the sea becomes very heavy and shock-like Visibility affected. | Seldom experienced; inland; trees uprooted; considerable structural damage occurs. | 48 to 55 |

| 11 | Violent storm | Exceptionally high waves. The sea is completely covered with long white patches of foam lying along the direction of the wind. Everywhere the edges of the wave crests are blown into froth. Visibility affected. | 56 to 63 |
| 12 | Hurricane | Air filled with foam and spray. Sea completely white with driving spray. Visibilty very seriously affected. | Greater than 63 |

# FRENCH BEAUFORT SCALE OF WIND FORCE

| Termes descriptif | | Vitesse moyenne en noeuds | Vitesse moyenne en km/h | Aspect de la mer dont on déduit la force du vent |
|---|---|---|---|---|
| 0 | Calme | inf. à 1 | inf. à 1 | Comme un miroir |
| 1 | Très légère bris | 1 - 3 | 1 - 5 | Quelques rides |
| 2 | Légère brise | 4 - 6 | 6 - 11 | Vaguelettes ne déferiant pas |
| 3 | Petite brise | 7 - 10 | 12 - 19 | Les moutons apparaissent |
| 4 | Jolie brise | 11 - 16 | 20 - 28 | Petites vagues, nombreux moutons |
| 5 | Bonne brise | 17 - 21 | 29 - 38 | Vagues modérées, moutons, embruns |
| 6 | Vent frais | 22 - 27 | 39 - 49 | Lames, crêtes d'écume blanche, embruns |
| 7 | Grand frais | 28 - 33 | 50 - 61 | Lames déferiantes, traînés d'écume |
| 8 | Coup de vent | 34 - 40 | 62 - 74 | Tourbilions d'écume à la crête des lames, traînées d'écume |
| 9 | Fort coup de vent | 41 - 47 | 75 - 88 | Lames déferiantes, grosses à énormes, visibilité réduite par les embruns |
| 10 | Tempête | 48 - 55 | 89 - 102 | Lames déferiantes, grosses à énormes, visibilité réduite par les embruns |
| 11 | Violente tempête | 56 - 63 | 103 - 117 | Lames déferiantes, grosses à énormes, visibilité réduite par les embruns |
| 12 | Ouragan | 64 et plus | 118 et plus | Lames déferiantes, grosses à énormes, visibilité réduite par les embruns |

Les vitesses se rapportent au vent moyen et non aux rafales.

## 4. TERMS USED IN WEATHER FORECASTS AND THEIR MEANINGS

### 1. Gale warnings

Warnings are issued for:

**Gales** if the mean wind is expected to increase to Force 8 (34 knots) or over, or gusts of 43 knots or over are expected. Gusts as high as 43 knots may occur with the mean wind below 34 knots in cold, unstable and showery airstreams.

**Severe gales** if the mean wind is expected to increase to Force 9 (41 knots) or over, or gusts of 52 knots or over are expected.

**Storm** if the mean wind is expected to increase to Force 10 (48 knots) or over or gusts of 61 knots are expected.
Winds above Force 10 can only be of academic interest to yachtsmen and will not be detailed here.

The words imminent, soon and later have precise meanings as follows:

*Imminent* – within 6 hours of issue of the warning.
*Soon* – 6 to 12 hours from time of issue.
*Later* – beyond 12 hours from time of issue.

### 2. Wind

The wind direction is always the direction from which the wind is blowing: veer means a clockwise change in wind direction, e.g. from west to northwest: back means an anticlockwise change in direction, e.g. from northwest to west.
In sea area forecasts wind strengths are always given in terms of the Beaufort Force. The table on the preceding two pages gives a very concise explanation.
In land area forecasts winds are always given in terms of moderate, fresh, etc. and these terms are defined as follows:

**Beaufort Force**

| | |
|---|---|
| Calm | 0 |
| Light | 1-3 |
| Moderate | 4 |
| Fresh | 5 |
| Strong | 6-7 |
| Gale | 8 |

### 3. Visibility

In sea area forecasts, visibility descriptions have the following meanings:

| | |
|---|---|
| Good | More than 5 nautical miles |
| Moderate | 2 to 5 nautical miles |
| Poor | 1,000 metres to 2 nautical miles |
| Fog | Less than 1,000 metres |

In land area reports and forecasts fog is described in more detail as follows:

| | |
|---|---|
| Fog | Visibility 200 to 1,000 metres |
| Thick Fog | Visibility less than 200 metres |
| Dense Fog | Visibility less than 50 metres |

In coastal station reports and aviation forecasts the definitions are:

| | |
|---|---|
| Mist or Haze | Visibility 1,000 to 2,000 metres |
| Fog | Visibility less than 1,000 metres |

## 4. Weather

This is not included in reports from automatic stations.

The terms rain, snow, hail etc are obvious enough but the use of the word fair calls for some definition. The weather is described as fair when there is nothing significant i.e. no rain, fog, showers, etc. It may or may not be cloudy.

## 5. Pressure and pressure tendency

The general synopsis often gives the values of the pressure at the centres of important weather systems, while the coastal station reports give recorded atmospheric pressure at a selection of stations and the pressure tendency. The millibar is the unit used for pressure in shipping bulletins and on most charts published in the press and elsewhere. Some countries have replaced millibar by hectopascal as the name for the standard unit of pressure. There is no numerical difference between the two.
One millibar (or mb) = one hectopascal (or hPa)

The terms used for pressure tendency in the coastal station reports are defined as follows:

| | |
|---|---|
| Steady | Change less than 0.1 mb in 3 hours |
| Rising slowly or<br>falling slowly | Change 0.1 to 1.5 mb in last 3 hours |
| Rising or falling | Change 1.6 to 3.5 mb in last 3 hours |
| Rising quickly or<br>falling quickly | Change 3.6 to 6.0 mb in last 3 hours |
| Rising or falling<br>very rapidly | Change of more than 6.0 mb in last 3 hours |
| Now falling,<br>now rising | Change from rising to falling or vice versa within last 3 hours |

BEWARE of reading too much into reports of rising slowly, falling slowly, now falling and now rising if general pressure changes are small. Every day there are small ups and downs in pressure all over the world due to the atmospheric tide. In the south of the UK the tidal pressure variation is just under 1 mb. At the equator it is 3 mbs. The highest values of pressure due to this tide are at 1000 and 2200, the lowest at 0400 and 1600: the same local times everywhere in the world. So if at 0400 and 1600 the pressure is reported as falling slowly it does not mean the weather is likely to or beginning to deteriorate. Similarly if at 1000 and 2200 the pressure is reported as rising slowly it says nothing about improvement in the weather.

## 6. The general synopsis and preamble to land area forecasts

### Depressions

A **depression** is synonymous with a **low** (i.e. low pressure system with a central vortex) or a **cyclone** (but only the relatively weak tropical cyclones are called depressions). A depression is a cyclonic vortex in the atmosphere in which the winds circulate anticlockwise in the northern hemisphere (clockwise in the southern hemisphere), and blow slightly inwards towards the centre. Depressions in middle latitudes vary enormously in size and energy. Their diameter may be anything from 100 to 2,000 miles with winds of from about 10 to over 70 knots at the surface and central pressure from below 950 millibars in a really deep depression to perhaps as high as 1,025 millibars in a very shallow one. Their speed of movement may be anything up to 60 knots. In a newly formed depression the circular spiralling motion of the air may extend upwards to only a thousand metres or so at most, while in an old depression it may extend upwards to over 15,000 metres.

A **deepening** depression is one in which the central pressure is falling, and in which the winds and rain must be expected to increase. In a **filling** depression the reverse applies. A **vigorous** depression may be large or small but is characterised by strong winds and a lot of rain. A **complex** depression has more than one centre of low pressure.

The simplest form of depression is a perfectly circular system in which the winds are the same speed all the way round and decrease gradually as you move out from the centre. The nearest approach to this ideal is found in the tropics, but in middle latitudes their shape and wind distribution vary greatly. In some, the strongest winds are near the centre, in others the strongest winds may be 500 miles out from the centre.

### Troughs of low pressure

In most depressions the cloud and rain tend to be concentrated in bands extending outwards from somewhere near the centre. These bands of weather may be from 10 to 200 miles wide and are called **troughs of low pressure** because the pressure is lower along them than at other points the same distance from the centre of the depression. There is a very definite relation between pressure and wind; the wind blows according to the gradient of pressure. The greater the fall of pressure from one point to the next the stronger the wind between the two points. So with a trough of low pressure; the more marked it is, the stronger the winds associated with it and the greater the change in the wind direction from one side of it to the other.

The simple diagram will help to make this point clearer.

ARROWS INDICATE WIND DIRECTION

D marks the centre of a depression. The line DA marks the axis of a **vigorous** trough of low pressure in which there is a change of wind of over 90 degrees as you go from one side to the other, you would expect a lot of rain mainly on the forward side of it. DB marks a less vigorous trough, but still with a quite a marked wind change and probably a fair amount of cloud and rain. DC is a relatively **weak** trough with comparatively little wind change and probably only occasional rain or a belt of showers.

Depressions can move in any direction but most frequently from west to east. Whether the depression is moving or not, its troughs will usually be circulating round its centre. If you are at X and the trough moves across you, you can see from the diagram that the winds will back and increase as the trough approaches and veer as it passes. The passage of even the weakest trough may make a lot of difference to your attempt to round a windward mark. If you are at X and the depression moves ENE to the north of you, the wind will veer from southerly ahead of the low to northerly behind it. The veer is unlikely to be steady and will in fact be concentrated in the passage of the troughs, while ahead of the troughs you may experience a temporary backing of the wind. This is typical of what is met with in practice, but there are an awful lot of variations on the theme. Finally, if you are at X and the depression moves ESE keeping its centre south of you, the winds will back from southerly to northerly. Any troughs will again be an added complication.

Troughs may fill or deepen independently of the parent depression, and sometimes a deepening trough will develop its own circulation and a new low is formed – a **secondary depression**.

## Fronts

There is little that need be said about fronts because they are simply a particular type of trough of low pressure, and troughs have been discussed in the previous paragraph. A front is, in fact, a trough of low pressure in which there is a change in air mass from one side to the other. In a **warm front** the air mass changes from cold to warm as the warm frontal trough passes, and in a **cold front** the air mass changes from warm to cold as it passes. The troughs at DB and DA are typical positions for warm and cold fronts respectively in the circulation of a depression, with the warm air in between them. Troughs in which there is an air mass change are usually more vigorous than those in which there is none. In fact wherever you find an air mass change you will usually find some sort of trough of low pressure. Fronts have a number of typical weather characteristics which are discussed in most books on the weather. Their wind change characteristics are the same as for the trough. Incidentally, in land area forecasts, fronts are rarely mentioned and are usually referred to as troughs. The same sometimes applies in the shipping forecasts.

## Anticyclone

The word anticyclone obviously means something contrasting with cyclone. An anticyclone or **high** has a high central pressure relative to its surroundings, fair or fine weather and light winds circulating clockwise around the centre in the northern hemisphere and anti-clockwise in the southern, and blowing slightly outwards. They vary in size from perhaps 200 miles across for the small high that accidentally finds itself between two lows, to some 2,500 miles across for some of the large and very persistent anticyclones which are responsible for the longer spells of dry weather. An anticyclone is said to **build** if its pressure is rising and to **decline** or **weaken** if its pressure is falling. If the pressure is falling very quickly it is said to be **collapsing**. Large anticyclones are usually slow-moving but some of the smaller ones which occur between depressions move quickly – perhaps as fast as 30 to 40 knots. More often, between depressions, instead of a high, with a closed circulation, one finds a **ridge of high pressure**. This is analogous to a mountain ridge between two hollows. Similarly a weak ridge may well occur between two troughs (or valleys) even in the circulation of a depression. The weather in a ridge is similar to the weather in an anticyclone though it may not last as long. In a weak ridge between two fast moving troughs it may be little more than a bright period.

As you move outwards from the centre of an anticyclone or away from the axis of a ridge the winds usually increase. If a ridge is crossing your course the winds will decrease as it approaches, back as it passes and then increase and continue to back depending on what is coming next.

The following terms are used in bulletins to describe the speed of movement of pressure systems:

| | |
|---|---|
| Slowly | up to 15 knots |
| Steadily | 15 – 25 knots |
| Rather quickly | 25 – 35 knots |
| Rapidly | 35 – 45 knots |
| Very rapidly | over 45 knots |

## 7. Standard definitions of State of Sea

| Height of waves (metres) | | Definition English | French |
|---|---|---|---|
| 0 | | calm – glassy | calme – plate |
| 0 | to 0.1 | calm – rippled | calme – ridée |
| 0.1 | to 0.5 | smooth | belle |
| 0.5 | to 1.25 | slight | peu agitée |
| 1.25 | to 2.5 | moderate | agitée |
| 2.5 | to 4 | rough | forte |
| 4 | to 6 | very rough | trés forte |
| 6 | to 9 | high | grosse |
| 9 | to 14 | very high | trés grosse |
| over | 14 | phenomenal | énorme ou exceptionelle |

Write down at least the General Synopsis, the forecast for the sea areas in which you will be sailing, the forecast for adjacent sea areas, the reports from coastal stations nearest to your area, and the outlook from the land area forecast. If you are sailing close inshore write down also the regional land area forecast particularly details about the wind.

Having got all this information you can use it to decide the best strategy and tactics. Whether you are ocean racing or merely crossing Lyme Bay, if you set off on the wrong tack for an expected change in wind it can cost you many hours.

If you are motoring and fail to appreciate that a wind change is going to coincide with an adverse tide it can give you a most uncomfortable and perhaps dangerous short steep sea, or make it impossible to cross the bar when you were intending to make port before dark.

Many such situations can be avoided by careful attention to the weather forecasts. The weather can change very quickly. Forecasts are on the air at least every six hours and you should listen to all of them. If your radio goes wrong put into harbour for repairs.

The following example will show you the sort of detail which you can glean from careful attention to the shipping bulletin.

The morning Shipping Forecast included the following:

General Synopsis – 'a trough of low pressure will move eastwards across the British Isles and is expected to lie from Viking to German Bight at midnight tonight'.

Sea Area Forecast – 'Humber, Thames, Dover – southwest veering northwest, 4 to 6; rain or drizzle followed by showers; moderate or poor with fog patches, becoming good'.

'Wight, Portland – southwest veering northwest, 3 to 4; rain or drizzle then showers; visibility moderate or poor with fog patches, becoming good'.

'Plymouth – northwest, 3 to 4; showers becoming fair; good'.

Let us assume that you are hoping to sail in sea area Dover. The wind force given for the group of areas which includes Dover is 4 to 6 but since the next group to Dover is given as 3 to 4 we can infer that the wind in Dover is likely to be at the Force 4 end of the range.

The southwesterly wind is obviously associated with the rain, drizzle and fog patches ahead of the trough of low pressure, and the northwesterly wind with the showers and good visibility behind the trough. The trough has all the characteristics of a cold front. The forecast of northwesterly winds for Plymouth tells us that the trough is already past that area and we can infer that it is moving over the western edge of Portland. We are told that it will be over German Bight by midnight so we can interpolate its movement between these two sea areas and get a reasonably good forecast of its time of crossing sea area Dover. Hence we can derive our own forecast of the time of veer of wind in Dover and the time of clearance of the rain, drizzle and fog. We can in fact plan a fair passage across the Channel from late morning onwards with a following wind, good visibility and just a few showers. The coastal stations reports from south coast stations would be found to confirm the inference as to the present position of the trough.

The more you practise the art the more interesting and useful you will find the bulletins and reports from all sources, even those for the more remote parts of southeast Iceland. Each item of information becomes a piece in a jig-saw which you need to complete the whole picture.

But what if your sources of information disagree or are inconsistent? Suppose Jersey Radio gives a different forecast from Niton, or Schevenigen tells a different story from North Foreland. It is no use denying that this happens. It does. But do not despair. Remember two things. First, that both forecasts must be based on the same initial data – they cannot be contrary in that sense; second that you already have, or should have, a good idea as to what the weather chart looks like in terms of depressions and anticyclones, troughs and ridges. This cannot be in dispute. So you, with your weather map in front of you, are in a good position to sort out for yourself what is the best possible forecast for your own particular area. You can even try to identify the reasons for the two divergent forecasts in terms of what is happening on the chart. And what is even more important, the lapse of time since the forecast was prepared means that you have additional information in terms of the weather you have observed and are observing which will help you to sort out the answer. What is the barometer doing, the wind, the cloud, and the sea. Even the smallest amount of information is all part of the overall pattern of movement and change in the atmosphere. And if you can go even a small way to understanding it, it will provide a new dimension to life afloat.

Metmap forms for constructing your own weather map are available from RYA, Romsey Road, Eastleigh, Hants SO5 4YA. Price £2.25 pack of 25.

More detailed guidance will be found in *Weather at Sea* – Chapters 1 and 2 (see page 4).

## 6. COASTAL WINDS

Winds within about 10 miles of the coast are influenced by the contours of the nearby land, by the local generation of the sea and land breezes, by the state of the tide, and by the fact that air blowing over water is subject to a different frictional force from air blowing over land. These coastal influences may cause a difference of as much as 10 to 15 knots in the wind at points only a few kilometres apart, even when the coast is fairly flat. Near mountains a local increase of 20-30 knots is not uncommon.

### Land and sea breezes
Land breezes are experienced at night. They are strongest under clear skies and at the mouths of valleys. Sea breezes develop when the land is warmer than the sea. They become strongest in the afternoon, when it is warm and sunny over land, and when the direction of the pressure gradient wind is from land to sea and from right to left looking seawards. For instance if you are on a south facing coast the strongest breeze occurs when the gradient wind is between north and west.

### Frictional effects
Land, particularly where there are trees and buildings, exerts a drag on the air. The drag over the water is much less. These frictional forces not only slow the air down but also cause a change of direction, and the direction over the water is about 15° different from the direction over the land. Winds blowing nearly parallel to the coast will converge or diverge depending on whether the greater friction is to the right or left of the wind direction. With convergence (east winds on a south facing coast, west winds on a north facing coast, etc) a band of stronger winds is experienced within about three miles of the coast; up to 10 knots stronger in some cases. Conversely with divergence (west winds on a south facing coast, etc) winds may be that much lighter near the coast; but in this case look for compensating sea breezes in the afternoon.

### Tidal effect
A change in tide causes a small change in friction and therefore in wind speed and direction which may sometimes be noticeable.

More detailed information will be found in *Wind Strategy* Second Edition 1992 by David Houghton in the Sail to Win Series published by Fernhurst Books.

# 7. WEATHER HAZARDS

## 1. Gales

Gales which are due to depressions do not spring up without any warning. All inshore sailors can avoid them and so too can many offshore sailors. Squalls and thunderstorms are a different matter and will be discussed later.

How does one receive warning of an approaching gale? The most obvious answer is to keep a listening watch on Radio 4 or the nearest coast radio station. The battery power consumption of most modern transistor radios is very small but carry spare batteries just in case. If you need to save power then switch in to Radio 4 on the hour or to the coast radio at the end of each silence period (3 and 33 minutes past each hour) – you will need an alarm clock to remind you.

Your barometer or barograph will also give you good warning of an approaching gale. A fall of pressure of over 8 millibars in 3 hours is almost certain to be followed by a gale whatever your wind is to start with, and a fall of pressure of over 5 millibars in 3 hours is almost certain to be followed by a Force 6 (the yachtsman's gale). If your wind is Force 3 or less when you observe these tendencies your barometer will have given you about 4 to 8 hours warning. A very rapid rise in pressure after a trough has passed is also indicative of a gale and the same figures apply – a rise of over 8 millibars in 3 hours for a Force 8 and over 5 millibars in 3 hours for a Force 6. You must of course make allowances for your own movement, either towards or away from the depression. Buy's Ballots Law – if you stand with your back to the wind low pressure is on your left hand side – will tell you which way you are going relative to the depression.

If the barometer is falling rapidly and clouds are increasing rapidly – particularly if the upper clouds are moving fast and are well veered to the surface winds – then fear the worst and do not be caught on a lee shore.

Slower changes in the barometer reading do not necessarily preclude a gale, but they are less definitive.

## 2. Strong local winds

If the wind is blowing almost parallel to the coast, or at an angle of up to about 25 degrees, then be prepared for a local increase of wind up to 10 miles from the coast. This is especially marked on the edges of anticyclones when a local increase of over 10 knots may occur. For instance, an easterly wind blowing down the English Channel in the circulation of an anticyclone to the north, while only Force 4 over most of the Channel, may be Force 6 or even 7 along the English coast. An outstanding example is with a northeasterly over Biscay when an increase of as much as 20 knots frequently occurs off Cape Finisterre.

Another wind which needs watching is the sea breeze. On a sunny summer's day, if conditions are right, the sea breeze may enhance the actual wind to give a local increase of a good 10 knots just along the coast. A gentle breeze in a warm and sheltered harbour is often unrepresentative of conditions out at sea.

## 3. Squalls and thunderstorms

The arched line of black cloud associated with a squall can usually be seen as it approaches and so it gives its own warning, but only a brief one, of about half an hour. The only thing to do is to reef and make for the lightest part of the cloud. Having weathered the squall you can usually take it that another one is unlikely for 4 to 6 hours.

The advancing dark mass of threatening cloud associated with a mature thunderstorm is distinguishable from that of an advancing depression by the lack of freshening wind and sea ahead of it. In fact, it is often heralded by a decrease in wind and an almost glassy sea. The best rule is to sail so as to leave the storm to port. By doing so, although you may not miss the associated squalls you should miss the worst of them. Your barometer or barograph will show very erratic pressure changes in a thunderstorm, jumping down and up by a millibar or two.

## 4. Fog

Two types of fog must be distinguished, land and sea fog.

**Land or radiation fog** – This is fog which forms over the land on a clear night. It may drift seawards from the coast but does not usually go far before dispersing, and rarely more than 2 to 3 miles from the shore. What is more, as soon as it hits the sea, it starts clearing near the surface and by the time it is 100 metres offshore it is usually clear to about mast height. So if the forecast is for fog over land, clearing during the morning, you can safely go out to sea expecting the fog to be gone by the time you return to port.

**Sea fog** – This is one of the worst hazards at sea and forms when warm moist air is carried by the wind over a relatively cold sea. The criterion for sea fog to form is when the dewpoint of the air is equal to or above the sea surface temperature. In winter and spring the sea is coldest inshore so fog forms more frequently along the coast than out to sea. In summer and autumn the sea is coldest away from the shore so fog forms more frequently out at sea. There are always variations in sea temperature from place to place and consequently variations in the extent of sea fog.

If the dewpoint of the air being blown across the sea is very high, and everywhere the sea temperature is lower, then **widespread fog** or **extensive fog** is forecast. If the dewpoint of the air is only a little above sea temperature and in some places may not be so, then **fog banks** are forecast. If the dewpoint of the air is only above the sea temperature in some places then **fog patches** are forecast, or, in winter and spring just **coastal fog** if that is appropriate.

**1. Location of Stations whose latest weather reports are broadcast in the BBC Radio 4 shipping bulletins**

\* Automatic stations, whose reports do not include:
  a) 'weather', ie if there is rain, drizzle, shower etc.
  b) visibility greater than 5 miles

**2. Location of Stations whose latest weather reports are broadcast in the BBC Radio 4 inshore waters bulletins**

## 3. Forecasts and weather reports by telephone & fax

### Marinecall, MetFAX Marine, and Weathercall

All the information on these services is from the Met Office. Their content is described on pages 7 and 8. Marinecall and Marinecall Fax are an integrated telephone and fax service for sailors and fishermen, the forecasts on fax being backed by weather maps. MetFAX Marine includes other useful information appropriate to fax only. Weathercall provides for sailors on inland waters.

### Marinecall and Marinecall Fax

| Service/product | Dialling prefix | Update times |
|---|---|---|
| Telephone 2-day forecast | 0891-500-XXX | 0700   1300†   1900 |
| Telephone 5-day planner | | 0500 |
| UK National | 0891-500-450 | |
| English Channel | -992 | |
| Southern North Sea | -991 | |
| Irish Sea | -942 | |
| Telephone latest weather reports | 0891-226-XXX | Hourly |
| Fax 2-day forecast plus latest | 0336-400-XXX | 0700   1300†   1900 |
| weather maps | | 0500            1700 |
| Fax 3-5day planner plus latest | | 0500 |
| weather maps | | 0800 |
| UK National | 0336-400-450 | |
| English Channel | -471 | |
| Southern North Sea | -472 | |
| Irish Sea | -473 | |

### Other MetFAX Services

Index pages dialling code

| | |
|---|---|
| MetFAX Marine | 0336-400-401 |
| MetFAX Aviation | 0336-400-501 |
| MetFAX Education | 0336-400-480 |

**MetFAX Marine**

| Product | Fax number | Update times | | |
|---|---|---|---|---|
| 24-hour shipping forecast | 0336-400-441 | 0030 | 0600 | |
| | | 1400 | 1800 | |
| Latest weather map* | -444 | 0340 | 0940 | |
| | | 1540 | 2140 | |
| 24-hour forecast weather map* | -445 | 0440 | 1040 | |
| | | 1640 | 2240 | |
| Chart of weather reports* | -447 | 0030 then every 3 hrs | | |
| 2-5 day NW Scottish waters | -468 | 0800 | 2000 | |
| 2-5 day Northern North Sea | -469 | 0800 | 2000 | |
| Satellite picture* | -499 | 0730 | 1330 | 1930 |

XXX   dial the 3 figures appropriate to the area you want – see Marinecall area map and list on next page

*   Update times one hour later when British Summer Time in force

†   For areas 455, 456, 457, 458 only


Calls on all these 0891 and 0336 numbers are charged at 49p per minute standard rate and 39p per minute cheap rate

For more information, problem solving etc there is a MetFAX helpline
Telephone: 0344 854435,  Fax: 0344 854018

## Marinecall and Marinecall Fax coastal areas

| | |
|---|---|
| 451 | Scotland North |
| 452 | Scotland East |
| 453 | North East |
| 454 | East |
| 455 | Anglia |
| 456 | Channel East |
| 457 | Mid-Channel |
| 458 | South West |
| 459 | Bristol Channel |
| 460 | Wales |
| 461 | North West |
| 462 | Clyde |
| 463 | Caledonia |
| 464 | Minch |
| 465 | Ulster |

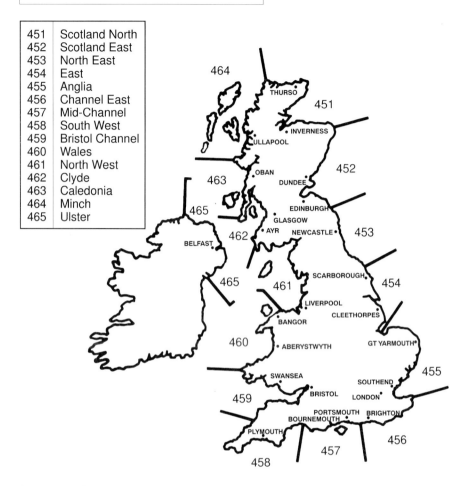

**Marinecall Club**

The Marinecall Club is a new and simple way of obtaining Marinecall forecasts for any of 15 UK coastal areas without paying premium rate call charges.

Membership to the club costs only £10 (this is a one off payment) and enables you to pre-pay for calls which can be bought in bulk units at a discount.

One unit equals one Marinecall forecast access.

Many modern telephones including payphones bleep when you dial out and these tones will activate Marinecall. However, telephones based in remote sites and abroad may require the use of a tone pad which is supplied when you join the Club. Members simply dial 071-971-0102, and upon answering you tap in your membership number and security code number, which is automatically allocated when you join.

To apply call Marinecall Customer Liaison Department on 071-975-9000, Fax 071-236-3501

## Weathercall
(Dialling prefix 0891 500)

| | |
|---|---|
| 400 | National |
| 401 | London |
| 402 | Kent, Sussex, Surrey |
| 403 | Dorset & Hants |
| 404 | Devon & Cornwall |
| 405 | Wilts, Gloucs, Avon & Somerset |
| 406 | Berks, Bucks & Oxon |
| 407 | Beds, Herts & Essex |
| 408 | Norfolk, Suffolk & Cambs |
| 409 | West, Mid, Sth Glam & Gwent |
| 410 | Shrops, Hereford & Worcester |
| 411 | Central Midlands |
| 412 | East Midlands |
| 413 | Lincs & Humberside |
| 414 | Dyfed & Powys |
| 415 | Gwynedd & Clwyd |
| 416 | N W England |
| 417 | W & S Yorks & Peak District |
| 418 | N E England |
| 419 | Cumbria, incl Lake District |
| 420 | S W Scotland |
| 421 | W Central Scotland |
| 422 | Ed'burgh, S Fife, Lothian & Borders |
| 423 | E Central Scotland |
| 424 | Grampian & E Highlands |
| 425 | N W Scotland |
| 426 | Caithness, Orkney & Shetland |
| 427 | N Ireland |
| 430 | National 3 to 5 day outlook |

Marinecall, MetFAX Marine and Weathercall are charged at 49p per minute (standard rate) and 39p per minute (evenings and weekends) including VAT.


## Weather routeing

A global weather routeing service including pre-voyage advice, planning, regular weather and wave forecasts, routeing advice while on passage and post-voyage analysis, is provided commercially by the Met Office. The METROUTE desk may be contacted on Tel: 0344-854904/5, Fax: 0344-854412 .

## Weather Centres and Met Offices

Calls may be made to the following Weather Centres, but it must be appreciated that with only one forecaster available to respond it may be difficult to get through. Consultations via special ex-directory numbers are available on pre-payment. Numbers can be obtained from Weather Centres.

|  | Telephone | Fax |
|---|---|---|
| Birmingham Weather Centre | 021-717-0570 | 021-717-0579 |
| Bristol Weather Centre | 0272-279298 | 0272-279060 |
| Cardiff Weather Centre | 0222-397020 | 0222-390435 |
| Leeds Weather Centre | 0532-451990 | 0532-457760 |
| London Weather Centre | 071-831-5968 | 071-242-3666 |
| Manchester Weather Centre | 061-477-1060 | 061-477-1068 |
| Newcastle Weather Centre | 091-232-6453 | 091-261-4965 |
| Norwich Weather Centre | 0603-660779 | 0603-629832 |
| Nottingham Weather Centre | 0602-384092 | 0602-385287 |
| Plymouth Weather Centre | 0752-251860 | 0752-251862 |
| Southampton Weather Centre | 0703-228844 | 0703-228846 |
| Aberdeen Weather Centre | 0224-210574 | 0224-210575 |
| Glasgow Weather Centre | 041-248-3451 | 041-248-3455 |
| Kirkwall Airport, Orkney | 0856-3802 | 0856-2892 |
| Sella Ness, Shetland | 0806-242069 | 0806-242070 |
| Belfast Airport | 08494-22339 | 08494-54091 |

Most Weather Centres are open for personal inquiries all day from Monday to Friday

## Noble Denton Weather Services Limited

Noble Denton Weather Services is a private weather forecasting company, which specialises in forecasting for marine operations and activities.

Noble Denton's Forecast Centre in Central London operates 24-hours a day, every day of the year and routinely receives global meteorological data including the output from several computer models of the atmosphere. Using this data, Nobel Denton's experienced forecasters can prepare meaningful and easy-to-understand weather forecasts, tailored to meet the specific requirements of the individual client.

Noble Denton's Weather Consultancy Service enables you to speak directly to a forecaster who has the latest information at his fingertips and can discuss your specific requirements. Instant up-to-date weather forecasts for any location in the UK or Europe, either onshore or offshore, can be supplied through this service.

Noble Denton can also supply regular detailed forecasts for up to 72 hours ahead, with a further outlook for up to seven days ahead, for any location in the world. These forecasts can be faxed or telexed.

Details and prices of services can be supplied upon request. For further information contact:

Noble Denton Weather Services Limited
Noble House
131 Aldersgate Street
London  EC1A 4EB
Tel: 071-606-4961   Fax: 071-606-5035

**Reports of actual local weather conditions may be obtained by telephone from the following stations:**

| Name of Station | Telephone No. | Type of Station |
|---|---|---|
| MRSC Stornoway | 0851-702013/4 | C G |
| Butt of Lewis | 0851-81201 | L H |
| Cape Wrath | 097181-230 | L H |
| Strathy Point | 06414-210 | L H |
| MRSC Pentland (Orkney) | 0856-873268 | C G |
| MRSC Lerwick (Shetland) | 0595-2976 | C G |
| Sella Ness | 0806-242069 | Met O |
| MRCC Aberdeen | 0224-592334 | C G |
| MRSC Forth (Fifeness) | 0333-50666 | C G |
| MRSC Tyne Tees | 091257-2691 | C G |
| Whitby | 0947-602107 | C G |
| MRSC Humber | 0262-672317 | C G |
| MRSC Yarmouth | 0493-851338 | C G |
| Cromer | 0263-512507 | C G |
| MRSC Thames | 0255-675518 | C G |
| MRCC Dover | 0304-210008 | C G |
| Eastbourne | 0323-20634 | C G |
| St. Catherine's Point | 0983-730284 | L H |
| MRSC Solent | 0705-552100 | C G |
| MRSC Portland | 0305-760439 | C G |
| Portland Bill | 0305-820495 | L H |
| MRSC Brixham | 0803-882704/5 | C G |
| MRCC Falmouth | 0326-317575/313053 | C G |
| Lizard | 0326-290431 | L H |
| MRCC Swansea | 0792-366534/367761 | C G |
| MRSC Milford Haven | 0646-690909 | C G |
| MRSC Holyhead | 0407-762051/763911 | C G |
| Rhyl | 0745-39749 | C G |
| MRSC Liverpool (Crosby) | 051931-3341/3343 | C G |
| MRSC Belfast (Bangor) | 0247-463933 | C G |
| Calf of Man | 0624-822820 | C G |
| Point of Ayre | 0624-880238 | L H |
| MRCC Clyde (Greenock) | 0475-29988/29014 | C G |
| Rhinns of Islay | 049681-223 | L H |
| Hyskeir | 0688-2423 | L H |
| MRSC Oban | 0631-63720/63729 | C G |

Key to Abbreviations

| | |
|---|---|
| C G | Coast Guard Station |
| L H | Lighthouse |
| Met O | Met Office |
| MRCC | Coastguard Maritime Rescue Co-ordination Centre |
| MRSC | Coastguard Maritime Rescue Co-ordination Sub-Centre |

MRCCs and MRSCs broadcast Met Office local inshore waters forecasts every 4 hours (gale and strong wind warnings every 2 hours) on Channel 67 after announcement on Channel 16.

## 4. Telephone weather services in France

France Telecom and Meteo-France operate an automatic telephone weather service - ALLO METEO FRANCE - with a universal number, the forecast heard depending on the area in which you call as follows:

| Service | Number |
|---|---|
| National forecast | 36 68 01 01 |
| Regional forecast | 36 68 00 00 |
| Departmental forecast | 36 68 02 XX |
| | (XX is the local departmental code) |
| Mountain forecast | 36 68 04 04 |
| Marine forecast | 36 68 08 08 |
| Marine local coastal forecast | 36 68 08 XX  (see below) |

While the marine forecast service number 36 68 08 08 is universally valid and provides a fairly detailed local coastal forecast, even more detail is available on the following numbers; prefixed in each case by 36 68 08.

| Coastal Zone | Telephone Number |
|---|---|
| Pas de Calais | 36 68 08 59 or 62 |
| Somme estuary | 80 |
| Seine estuary | 76 |
| Calvados | 11 |
| Cotentin | 50 |
| Ille et Vilaine | 35 |
| Côtes d'Armor | 22 |
| Finistère | 29 |
| Morbihan | 56 |
| Loire-Atlantique | 44 |
| Vendée | 85 |
| Charente maritime | 17 |
| Gironde | 33 |
| Landes | 40 |
| Pyrénées Atlantiques | 64 |

Mediterranean

| | |
|---|---|
| Cerbère à Narbonne to the Balearics | 36 68 08 66 or 11 |
| Narbonne to Port Camargue | 30  or 34 or 11 |
| Mouth of the Rhône | 30  or 13 |
| Var | 83 |
| Alpes Maritimes | 06 |
| Corsica, east and west coasts | 20 |

The cost of this service is independent of distance and at a universal rate of 2.19 Frs per minute.

## 5. Radio Facsimile Broadcasts

A great deal of weather information including observations and actual and forecast weather charts may be received by ships at sea on the following continuous radio facsimile broadcasts.

|  | Time | Call Sign | Frequency (kHz) | |
|---|---|---|---|---|
| United Kingdom – Bracknell |  | GFA | 3289.5 | |
|  |  |  | 4782 | |
|  |  |  | 8040 | |
|  |  |  | 9203 | |
|  |  |  | 11086.5 | |
|  |  |  | 14436 | |
| UK – Northwood | Transmission |  | 2374 | 8331.5 |
|  | Schedule |  | 3652 | 12844.5 |
|  | broadcast at |  | 4307 | 16912 |
|  | 0300 and 1640 |  | 6446 | |
| Germany – Offenbach | 0400-2300 | DDH3 | 3855 | |
| Pinneburg | Transmission | DDK3 | 7880 | |
|  | Schedule | DDK6 | 13882.5 | |
|  | broadcast on |  |  | |
|  | Monday at 1040 |  |  | |
| Italy – Rome |  | IMB51 | 4777.5 | |
|  |  | IMB55 | 8146.6 | |
|  |  | IMB56 | 13597.4 | |
| Spain – Rota | Transmission | ADK | 4704 | 9875 |
| (input from USA) | Schedule |  | 5785 | 17585 |
|  | broadcast at |  | 9382.5 | |
|  | 0003 and 2349 |  |  | |

## 6. NAVTEX

Message category codes and transmitting stations in Navarea 1

| | | | | | | |
|---|---|---|---|---|---|---|
| A | – | Navigational warning | | [B] | – | Bodo |
| B | – | Gale warning | | [G] | – | Cullercoats |
| C | – | Ice report | | [H] | – | Harnosand |
| D | – | Search and Rescue information | | [J] | – | Stockholm |
| E | – | Weather forecast | | [L] | – | Rogaland |
| F | – | Pilot service message | | [O] | – | Portpatrick |
| G | – | DECCA messages | | [P] | – | Scheveningen |
| H | – | LORAN messages | | [R] | – | Reykjavik |
| I | – | OMEGA messages | | [S] | – | Niton |
| J | – | SATNAV messages | | [T] | – | Ostend |
| K | – | Other electronic navaid messages | | [U] | – | Tallinn |
| L | – | Navigational warnings - additional to A | | [V] | – | Vardo |
| Z | – | No messages on hand | | | | |

**NAVTEX transmissions**

Gale warnings are broadcast by NAVTEX on receipt.

24-hour forecast weather bulletins and gale warnings are broadcast by the UK NAVTEX service according to the following schedule:

*Times GMT*      *Forecast areas*

0848 2048      Viking, North Utsire, South Utsire, Forties, Cromarty, Forth, Tyne, Dogger, Fisher, German Bight, Humber, Thames, Dover, Wight, Fair Isle and Faeroes

0818 2018      Thames, Dover, Wight, Portland, Plymouth, Biscay, Finisterre, Sole, Lundy, Fastnet, Irish Sea, Shannon, Rockall and Malin

0930 2130      Lundy, Fastnet, Irish Sea, Shannon, Rockall, Malin, Hebrides, Fair Isle, Faeroes and South-East Iceland

## 7. Schedule of weather bulletins and storm/gale warnings services available to yachtsmen in West European waters

### (Transmitted in plain language by radio telephony)

In the following schedule, the references to Areas are those indicated on the chart of the appropriate country which follow the schedule.

The key to the abbreviations used is as follows:

A    Full weather bulletin and forecast.
B    Strong wind and storm warnings or gale warnings.
C    Forecast for coastal waters only.
D    Wind forecast
2    Sea area boundaries as for United Kingdom
3    Gale warning summaries for appropriate sea areas are broadcast at 0303, 0903, 1503, 2103.
4    See chart for appropriate country.
7    Strong wind and gale warning summaries for local area only are broadcast at 0645, 1345, 1845, 2245, GMT. Strong wind warnings issued for Force 7, or gusts to Force 8.
8    Clock times.
9    H + 03, H + 33 until period of validity then change to time given in brackets.
†    Retransmission of earlier broadcast.
*    See also pages 5 to 8.

NOTES
In addition to the scheduled services shown a number of stations broadcast strong wind/ gale warnings on receipt and at the end of the next silence period after receipt.

If it is necessary to convert from kHz into metres divide kHz into 300,000 e.g.

$$200 \text{kHz} \quad = \quad \frac{300,000}{200} \quad = \quad 1500 \text{ Metres}$$

Some broadcasts give wind speed in metres per second. For conversion to knots multiplication by 2 is near enough.
1 Knot    =  0.515 m/sec.
1 m/sec  =  1.94 Knots.

Yachtsmen familiar with morse may wish to listen to the Atlantic Weather Bulletins for shipping, broadcast twice daily by W/T from Portishead Radio on 4286, 8545.9, 12822, 17098.4 and 22467 kHz. They are in six parts. Parts 1, 2, 3, 5 and 6 may be heard at 0930 and 2130 GMT and Part 4 at 1130 GMT.
The areas are as follows:

| | | |
|---|---|---|
| East Northern Section | 55°-65°N, | 15°-27$^1$/$_2$°W |
| West Northern Section | 55°-65°N, | 27$^1$/$_2$°-40°W |
| East Central Section | 45°-55°N, | 15°-27$^1$/$_2$°W |
| West Central Section | 45°-55°N, | 27$^1$/$_2$°-40°W |
| East Southern Section | 35°-45°N, | 15°-27$^1$/$_2$°W |
| West Southern Section | 35°-45°N, | 27$^1$/$_2$°-40°W |

| Station | Channel | Frequency kHz | Times of broadcast GMT | Sea areas[4] | Information given | Language |
|---|---|---|---|---|---|---|
| ALL stations on this page broadcast information for ALL sea areas listed below | | | | | | |

**United Kingdom***

| Station | Channel | Frequency kHz | Times of broadcast GMT | Sea areas[4] | Information given | Language |
|---|---|---|---|---|---|---|
| Portpatrick | 27 | 1883 | 0703 1903 | | | |
| Cardigan Bay | 03 | | 0703 1903 | | | |
| Anglesey | 26 | | 0703 1903 | | | |
| Morecambe Bay | 04 | | 0703 1903 | | | |
| Clyde | 26 | | 0703 1903 | | | |
| Oban | 07 | | 0703 1903 | North & South Utsire | | |
| Islay | 25 | | 0703 1903 | Forties Cromarty | | |
| Hebrides | 26 | 1866 | 0703 1903 | Forth Tyne | | |
| Skye | 24 | | 0703 1903 | Dogger Fisher | | |
| Lewis | 05 | | 0703 1903 | German Bight Humber Thames | A[3] | English |
| Wick | | 1764 | 0703 1903 | Lundy Irish Sea | | |
| Collafirth | 24 | | 0703 1903 | Rockall Malin | | |
| Shetland | 27 | 1770 | 0703 1903 | Hebrides Bailey | | |
| Orkney | 26 | | 0703 1903 | Fair Isle Faeroes | | |
| Cromarty | 28 | | 0703 1903 | South East Iceland | | |
| Stonehaven | 26 | 2691 | 0703 1903 | | | |
| Buchan | 25 | | 0703 1903 | | | |
| Forth | 24 | | 0703 1903 | | | |
| Cullercoats | 26 | 2719 | 0703 1903 | | | |
| Whitby | 25 | | 0703 1903 | | | |

| Station | Channel | Frequency kHz | Times of broadcast GMT | Sea areas[4] | Information given | Language |
|---|---|---|---|---|---|---|
| ALL stations in the first section of this page broadcast information for ALL sea areas listed | | | | | | |
| Humber | 26 | 1869 | 0733 1933 | | | |
| Grimsby | 27 | | 0733 1933 | | | |
| Bacton | 07 | | 0733 1933 | | | |
| North Foreland | 26 | 1848 | 0733 1933 | Tyne Dogger German Bight | | |
| Orfordness | 62 | | 0733 1933 | Humber Thames | | |
| Thames | 02 | | 0733 1933 | Dover Wight | | |
| Hastings | 07 | | 0733 1933 | Portland Plymouth | A[3] | English |
| Niton | 28 | 1641 | 0733 1933 | Biscay Finisterre | | |
| Weymouth | 05 | | 0733 1933 | Sole Lundy | | |
| Lands End | 27 64 | 2670 | 0733 1933 | Fastnet Irish Sea Shannon | | |
| Start Point | 26 | | 0733 1933 | | | |
| Pendennis | 62 | | 0733 1933 | | | |
| Ilfracombe | 05 | | 0733 1933 | | | |
| Celtic | 24 | | 0733 1933 | | | |
| Jersey | 25,82 | 1659 | 0645 0745 1245 1845 2245 | Waters around Channel Is., south of 50°N and east of 3°W | A[7] | English |
| BBC Radio 4[8] | | 198 and VHF | 0033 0555 1355 1750 | All U.K. sea areas | A | English |
| BBC Radio 3[8] | | 90.2-92.4mHz | 0655 | U.K. inshore waters | A | English |
| BBC Radio 4[8] and Radio Scotland | | 198 810 | 0038 approx | England, Wales & Scottish inshore waters | C | English |
| BBC Radio Ulster[8] | | 1341 | 0010 | Ulster inshore waters | C | English |

| Station | Channel | Frequency kHz | Times of broadcast GMT | Sea areas[4] | Information given | Language |
|---|---|---|---|---|---|---|
| RAF Volmet | | 4722 11200 | continuous | (see page 9) | | |
| London Volmet (main) | | 135.375mHz | | | | |
| London Volmet (south) | | 128.600mHz | continuous | (see page 9) | | |
| London Volmet (north) | | 126.600mHz | | | | |
| Scottish Volmet | | 125.725mHz | | | | |
| **Belgium** | | | | | | |
| Ostend | 27 | 2761 | 0820 1720 | Dover, Thames | A | English & Dutch |
| **Croatia** | | | | | | |
| Bar | 24 | 2752 | 0850 1420 2050 | Adriatic | A | National & English |
| Zagreb Radio[8] | | 98 89mHz | summer only 0800 1130 1800 | Adriatic | A | English German & Italian |
| Dubrovnik | 04,07 25 | | 0625 1320 2120 | Adriatic | A | National & English |
| Dubrovnik | | 105mHz | summer only 1800 | Adriatic | A | English |
| Split | 23,28 84 | 2685 | 0545 1245 1945 | Adriatic | A | National & English |
| Rijeka | 24 | 2771 | 0535 1435 1935 | Adriatic | A | National & English |
| **Denmark** | | | | | | |
| Blavand | 02, 23 | 1734 | On receipt & half-hour | North Sea and Baltic | B | Danish & English |
| Lyngby | 02,03 65,83 | 1704 | On receipt & half-hour | North Sea and Baltic | B | Danish & English |
| Danmarks Radio[8] | | 243 1062 | 0450 0750 1050 1650 2150 | North Sea and Baltic | A | Danish |

| Station | Channel | Frequency kHz | Times of broadcast GMT | Sea areas[4] | Information given | Language |
|---|---|---|---|---|---|---|
| Ronne | 04 | 2586 | On receipt & half-hour | North Sea and Baltic | B | Danish & English |
| Skagen | 01,04 64,66 | 1758 | On receipt & half-hour | North Sea and Baltic | B | Danish & English |
| **Finland** | | | | | | |
| Helsinki Radio[8] | | 1719 2810 | 0833 2033 | Gulf of Finland and Ålands | C | English |
| Mariehamn Radio[8] | 05,07 23,27 | 1779 | 0833 2033 | Gulf of Finland | C | English |
| **France** | | | | | | |
| Arcachon | | 1862 2755 | 0703 1903 H+03, H+33 | South Biscay, Finisterre | A | French |
| | | 1710 | (Even H+07)[9] | South Biscay, Finisterre | B | French |
| Boulogne | | 1692 3795 | 0703 1833 | North Sea and Channel | A | French |
| | | 1770 | H+03, H+33 (Odd H+03)[9] | North Sea and Channel | B | French |
| Le Conquet | | 1671 1876 2691 3722 | 0600 0733 1833 | Channel and areas west (West Portugal only at 0600) | A | French |
| | | 1635 | H+03, H+33 (Even H+33)[9] | Channel and areas west | B | French |
| St Nazaire | | 1722 2740 | 0803 1833 | Channel & areas west | A | French |
| | | 1686 | H+03, H+33 (Odd H+07)[9] | Channel & areas west | B | French |
| Grasse | | 2649 3722 | 0703 1303 1803 | West Mediterranean | A | French |
| | | 2649 3722 | H+03, H+33 (Even H+33)[9] | West Mediterranean | B | French |
| Marseille | | 1906 3795 | 0703 1303 1803 | West Mediterranean | A | French |
| | | 1906 3795 | H+03, H+33 (Odd H+10)[9] | West Mediterranean | B | French |

| Station | Channel | Frequency kHz | Times of broadcast GMT | Sea areas[4] | Information given | Language |
|---|---|---|---|---|---|---|
| Radio France (inter) | | 162 | 0650 Sat, Sun 1005 Mon-Fri 2005 Daily | All Sea areas | A | French |
| Ajaccio, Brest, | | 1404 | 0655 | All sea areas | A | French |
| Bastia, Bayonne | | 1494 | | | | |
| Bordeaux | | 1206 | | | | |
| Lille | | 1377 | | | | |
| Limoges | | 792 | | | | |
| Marseille | | 1242 | | | | |
| Nice | | 1557 | | | | |
| Paris | | 864 | | | | |
| Rennes | | 711 | | | | |
| Toulouse | | 945 | | | | |

Local coastal waters forecasts are broadcast as follows at local times after call on Channel 16.

| Transmitter | Channel | Times of broadcast | Coastal Zone |
|---|---|---|---|
| Dunkirk | 61 | 0733 1533 | Dunkirk to the Somme |
| Calais | 87 | | |
| Boulogne | 23 | | |
| Dieppe | 2 | 0733 1533 | Somme to the Seine |
| Le Havre | 26 | | |
| Port en Bessin | 3 | | |
| Cherbourg | 27 | | |
| St Malo | 2 | 0733 1533 | Havre to Penmarch |
| Paimpol | 84 | 0733 1533 | Havre to Penmarch |
| Plougasnou | 81 | | Pointe du Raz to Vendee |
| Ouessant | 82 | | |
| Le Conquet | 26 | | |
| Pont l'Abbe | 86 | | |
| Belle-Ile | 25 | 0733 1533 | Pointe du Raz to Vendee |
| St Nazaire | 23 | | |
| Nantes | 28 | | |
| St Gilles Croix de Vie | 27 | | |
| La Rochelle | 21 | 0733 1233 | The Charente Maritime to Spain |
| Royan | 23 | | |
| Arcachon | 82 | | |
| Bayonne | 24 | | |

| Transmitter | Channel | Times of broadcast | Coastal Zone |
|---|---|---|---|
| Perpignan | 2 | 0733 1233 | Port Vendres to Menton |
| Sete | 19 | | and the Corse |
| Martigues | 28 | | |
| Marseille | 26 | | |
| Toulon | 62 | | |
| Ajaccio | 24 | | |
| Grasse | 2 | | |
| Cavalaire | 4 | | |
| Bastia | 65 | | |
| Porto Vecchio | 5 | | |

| Station | Channel | Frequency kHz | Times of broadcast GMT | Sea areas[4] | Information given | Language |
|---|---|---|---|---|---|---|
| **Germany** | | | | | | |
| Nord and Westdeutscher Rundfunk[8] | | 558 576 657 702 729 972 | 2305 | German Bight, SW and Central North Sea, West and mid Baltic | A | German |
| Radio Bremen | | 936 6190 | 0928 2200 | German Bight Southern North Sea and West Baltic | C A | German German |
| Deutschlandfunk[8] | | 1269 1539 | 0005 0540 0005 | East North Sea, West and mid Baltic | A | German |
| Kiel[8] | | 2775 2775 | 0750 1950 0233 0633 1033 1433 1833 2233 | Baltic Baltic | A B | German German & English |
| Ruegen | 01,05, 21,23 | 1722 | 0810 2010 0730 1930 | Baltic | C | German & English |
| **Gibraltar** | | 1458 | 0445 0530 0630 0830 1030 2157 | up to 50nm from Gibraltar | A | English |
| **Greece** | | | | | | |
| Athens Radio | | 2590 | 0703 0933 1503 2103 | Greek waters | A | Greek & English |
| Chios Radio | | 1820 | 0703 0903 1533 2133 | Greek waters | A | Greek & English |

| Station | Channel | Frequency kHz | Times of broadcast GMT | Sea areas[4] | Information given | Language |
|---------|---------|---------------|------------------------|--------------|-------------------|----------|
| Hellenic Radio/TV | | 729 927 1044 1494 1512 1602 | 0430 1330 | All areas All areas | A A | Greek & English Greek |
| Heraklion Radio | | 2799 | 0703 0903 1533 2133 | Greek waters | B | Greek & English |
| Kerkyra Radio | | 2830 | 0703 0903 1533 2133 | Greek waters | A | Greek & English |
| Limnos Radio | | 2730 | 0703 0903 1533 2133 | Greek waters | A | Greek & English |
| **Ireland**[8] Radio Eireann | | 567,729 | 0633 1253 1823 1825 (Sat & Sun) 2355 (Mon-Fri only) | Irish waters within 30 miles of coast and Irish Sea | C C | English |
| Malin Head Cork Shannon Dublin | 23 26 28 83 | | 0103 0403 0703 1003 1303 1603 1903 2203 | Irish coastal waters up to 30 miles offshore and Irish Sea | A | English |
| Valentia Valentia | 24 | 1752 | 0833 2033 | Fastnet, Shannon Fastnet, Shannon | A A | English English |
| Shannon Volmet | | 3413 night 5505 8957 13264 day | continuous | (see page 9) | | |
| Dublin Volmet | 127.0mHz | | continuous | | | |
| **Italy** Ancona | 25 | 2656 | 0148 0748 1348 1948 | Areas 12, 13 | A | Italian & English |
| Augusta | 26 | 2628 | 0150 0750 1350 1950 | Areas 8, 9 | A | Italian & English |
| Bari | 26,27 | 2579 | 0125 0725 1325 1925 | Areas 8, 9, 10, 11 | A | Italian & English |

| Station | Channel | Frequency kHz | Times of broadcast GMT | Sea areas[4] | Information given | Language |
|---|---|---|---|---|---|---|
| Cagliari | 25,26,27 | 2680 | 0135 0735 1335 1935 | Areas 3, 4, 6 | A | Italian & English |
| Civitavecchia | 27 | 1888 | 0135 0735 1335 1935 | Areas 5, 6 | A | Italian & English |
| Crotone | 25 | 2663 | 0150 0750 1350 1950 | Areas 9,10 | A | Italian & English |
| Genova | 25, 27 | 2642 2722 | 0135 0735 1335 1935 | Areas 1, 2, 5 | A | Italian & English |
| Lampedusa | 26 | 1876 | 0150 0750 1350 1950 | Area 8 | A | Italian & English |
| Livorno | 26, 84 | 2591 | 0135 0735 1335 1935 | Areas 1, 5, 6 | A | Italian & English |
| Mazara del Vallo | 25 | 2211 | 0150 0750 1350 1950 | Area 8 | A | Italian & English |
| Messina | 25 | 2789 | 0135 0735 1335 1935 | Areas 7, 9, 10 | A | Italian & English |
| Napoli | 25, 27 | 2632 | 0135 0735 1335 1935 | Areas 6, 7 | A | Italian & English |
| Palermo | 27 | 1705 | 0135 0735 1335 1935 | Areas 7, 8 | A | Italian & English |
| Port Cervo | 26, 28, 85 | | 0150 0750 1350 1950 | Areas 6,7 | A | Italian & English |
| Port Torres | 26 | 2719 | 0150 0750 1350 1950 | Areas 2, 3, 6 | A | Italian & English |
| Radio Italia[8] (Radiodue) | | 846 936 1035 1116 1188 1314 1431 1449 | 0621 1432 2223 | All Italian sea areas | A | Italian |
| Ravenna | 27 | | 0150 0750 1350 1950 | Areas 12,13 | A | Italian & English |

| Station | Channel | Frequency kHz | Times of broadcast GMT | Sea areas[4] | Information given | Language |
|---------|---------|---------------|------------------------|--------------|-------------------|----------|
| Roma | 25 | | 0135 0735 1335 1935 | Areas 5, 6 | A | Italian & English |
| S. Benedetto del Tronto | | 1855 | 0150 0750 1350 1950 | Area 12 | A | Italian & English |
| Trapani | 25 | 1922 | 0150 0750 1350 1950 | Areas 7, 8 | A | Italian & English |
| Trieste | 25 | 2624 | 0135 0735 1335 1935 | Areas 12, 13 | A | Italian & English |
| Venezia | 26 | 2698 | 0150 0750 1350 1950 | Areas 12, 13 | A | Italian & English |
| **Monaco** | | | | | | |
| Monaco | | 8728 13172.1 13172 | 0715 1830 | West Med | A | French & English |
| Monaco | 23 | | continuous broadcast | St Raphael to San Remo, | A | French |
| Monaco | 3 | | continuous broadcast | Ligure, Corsica | A | Italian |
| Monaco[8] | 22 | 4363.6 | 0903 1403 1915 | Lion, Provence, Genes, Corse, Ouest Sardaigne Nord Baleares | A | French & English |
| **Malta** | | | | | | |
| Malta | 04 | 2625 | 0603 1003 1603 2103 | Maltese coastal waters up to 50 miles offshore | C | English |
| **Netherlands** | | | | | | |
| Scheveningen | | 1713 1890 | 0340 0940 1540 2140 | North Sea and Netherlands coastal waters | A | Dutch & English |
| Scheveningen[8] | 23, 25 27, 83 | | 0605 1205 1805 2305 | Netherlands coastal waters | C | Dutch |
| Amsterdam Volmet | | 126.2mHz | continuous | (see page 9) | | |

| Station | Channel | Frequency kHz | Times of broadcast GMT | Sea areas[4] | Information given | Language |
|---|---|---|---|---|---|---|
| **Norway** | | | | | | |
| Rogaland Radio | | 6507 8749 13158 | 1205 2305 | Coastal waters of South Norway and North Sea | A | Norwegian & English |
| **Portugal** | | | | | | |
| Leixões | | 2657 | 0730 1930 | Rio Minho to Cabo Carvoeiro | C | Portuguese |
| Cascais | | 2657 | 0800 2000 | Cabo Carvoeiro to Cabo De S. Vincente | C | Portuguese |
| Sagres | | 2657 | 0830 2030 | Cabo de S. Vincente to Rio Guadiana | C | Portuguese |
| (Portuguese Radio) Lisboa Azurara Porto Coimbra | | 666 720 1367 1449 | 0605[8] (March- Sept) 0705[8] (Oct -April) | Portuguese coastal waters and Madeira | C | Portuguese |
| **Spain** | | | | | | |
| Cabo de Penas Finisterre La Coruna Machichaco | | 1677 1764 1698 1707 | 1103 1733 | Gran Sol, Vizcaya, Cantabrico, Finisterre | A | Spanish |
| Tarifa Chipiona | | 1704 1656 | 1103 1733 | San Vincente, Cadiz, Alboran | A | Spanish |
| Barcelona Cabo de Gata Cabo de la Nao | | 1653 1767 1731 | 1103 1733 | Palos, Leon, Baleares, Argelia | A | Spanish |
| Radio Nacional[8] de Espana | | 585 639 684 729 738 774 855 | 1000 1300 1700 2100 | All coasts of Spain | A | Spanish |
| **Sweden** | | | | | | |
| Goteborg | 24, 26 82 | 1710 | 1033 2233 | Baltic | A | Swedish & English |

| Station | Channel | Frequency kHz | Times of broadcast GMT | Sea areas[4] | Information given | Language |
|---|---|---|---|---|---|---|
| Harnosand | | 1779 2733 | 0833 2033 | N. Baltic | A | Swedish & English |
| Karlskrona | | 2789 | 0954 2154 | Baltic | A | Swedish & English |
| Stockholm Radio | | 1674 | 0933 2133 | Baltic | A | Swedish & English |
| Tingstade | | 2768 | 1006 2206 | Baltic | A | Swedish & English |
| **Turkey** Antalya Bodrum Istanbul Izmir Samsun | 67 | | 1100 1400 1700 2000 2300 | | C | Turkish & English |

46

# UNITED KINGDOM

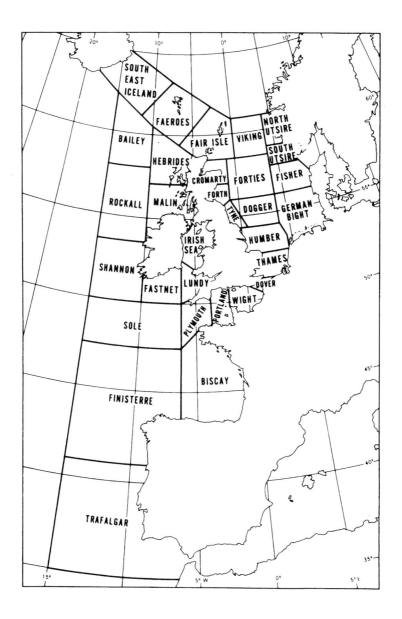

# NORTH SEA COMMON AREAS

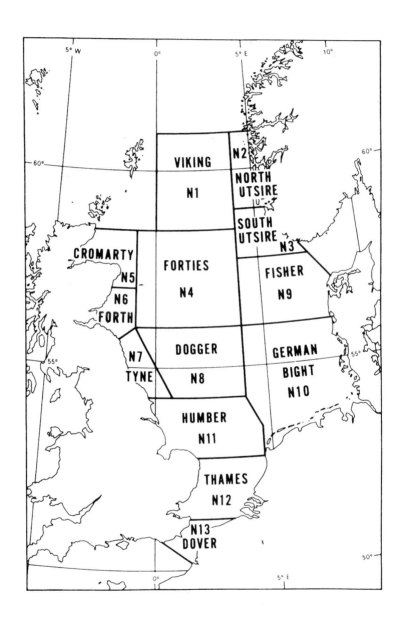

## FRANCE (North Sea areas on previous page)

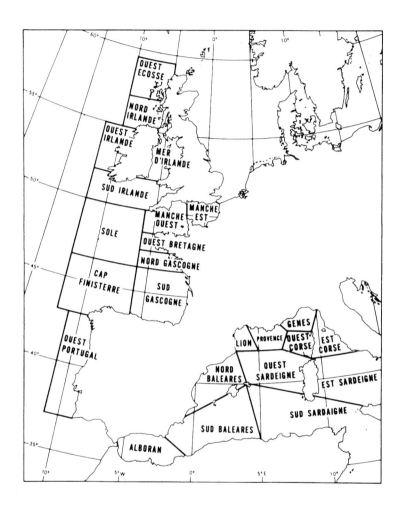

# BALTIC COMMON AREAS

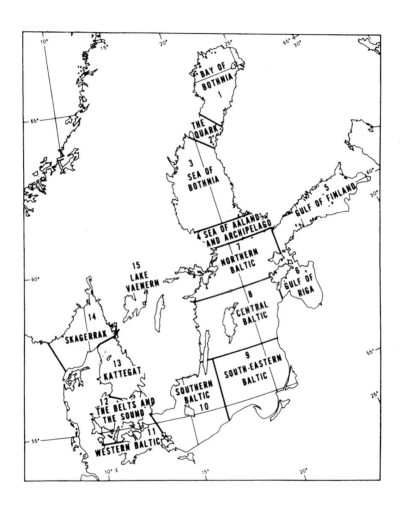

# SPAIN

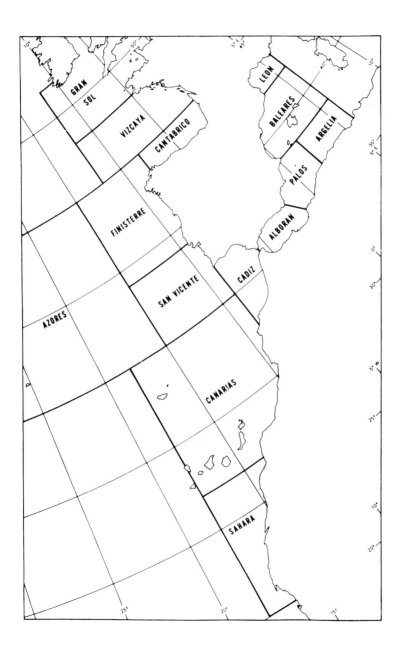

# ITALY

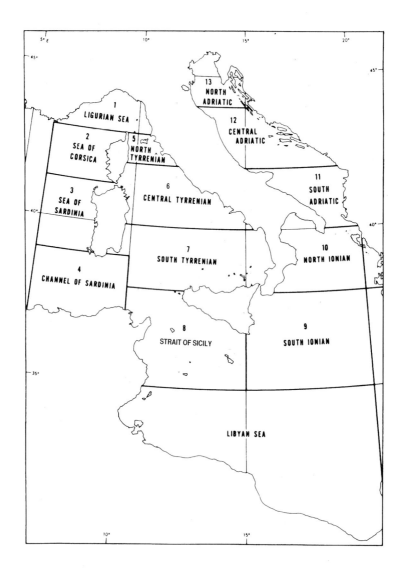

# GREECE

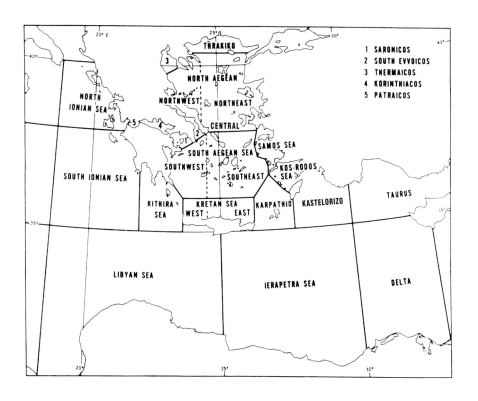

| | |
|---|---|
| 1 | SARONICOS |
| 2 | SOUTH EVVOICOS |
| 3 | THERMAICOS |
| 4 | KORINTHIACOS |
| 5 | PATRAICOS |

# 9. International weather vocabulary

| ENGLISH | DANISH | DUTCH | FRENCH | GERMAN | ITALIAN | SPANISH |
|---|---|---|---|---|---|---|
| Amendment | Aendring | Verandering | Changement Amendement | Anderung | Correzione | Enmienda Rectification |
| Area | Farvand | Gebied | Zone | Gebiet | Area | Zona |
| | | | | | | |
| Backing | Venstredrejende | Krimpend | Recul du vent | Rückdrehend | Rotazione a Sinistra Rotazione Antioraria | Rolada a la Izquierda |
| Beaufort Wind Scale | Beaufort's Vindskala | Beaufortschaal voor Windkracht | Echelle de Beaufort | Beaufortskala | Scala di Beaufort | Escala Beaufort |
| | | | | | | |
| Calm | Vindstille | Windstilte | Calme | Windstille | Calmo | Calma |
| Centre | Centrum Center | Centrum | Centre | Zentrum | Centro | Centro |
| Choppy | Skiftende | Woelig | Hachée | Kabbelige | Mosso | Agitado |
| Clouds | Skyer | Wolken | Nuages | Wolken | Nubi | Nubes |
| Clouds (broken) | Skyet | Gebroken | Nuages Fragmentés Troué | Bewölkung | Nubirotte | Quebrado, Nubes Fragmentadas |
| Cloudy | Overskyet | Bewolkt | Nuageux | Bewölkt | Nuvoloso | Nublado, Nuboso |
| Coast | Kyst | Kust | Côte | Küste | Costa | Costa |
| Coastal | Kyst- | Kust- | Littoral | An den Küste | Costiero | Costero |
| Cold | Kold | Koud | Froid | Kalt | Freddo | Frio |
| Cyclonic | Cyklonisk | Cycloonachtig, Cyclonisch | Cyclonique | Zyklonisch | Ciclonico | Ciclonica |
| | | | | | | |
| Dawn | Daggry | Dageraad Morgenschemering | Aube, au point du jour | Morgen-dämmerung | Alba | Alba |
| Decrease (Wind) | Aftagen | Afnemen | Affaiblissement, Diminution | Abnahme | Caduto, Diminuzione | Disminución |
| Deep | Dyb | Diep | Profond | Tief | Profondo | Profundo |
| Deepening | Uddybende | Verdiepend | Creusement | Vertiefung | Approfondi-mento | Ahondamiento |
| Dense | Taet, Tyk | Dicht | Dense | Dicht | Denso | Denso |
| Depression (Low) | Lavtryk | Depressie | Dépression | Tief | Depressione | Depresión |
| Direction | Retning | Richting | Direction | Richtung | Direzione | Dirreción |
| Dispersing | Som spreder sig | Verstrooiend | Se dispersant, se dissipant | Zerstreuung | Dispersione | Disipación |
| Drizzle | Finregn | Motregen | Bruine | Sprühregen | Spruzzatore, | Lloviznaa |

| ENGLISH | DANISH | DUTCH | FRENCH | GERMAN | ITALIAN | SPANISH |
|---------|--------|-------|--------|--------|---------|---------|
| Dusk | Tusmørke | Avondschem-ering | Brune, crépuscule du soir | Abend-dämmerung | Pioviggne Crepusculo Tramontana | Crepúsculo |
| East | Øst | Oosten | Est | Ost | Est Levante | Este |
| Eight | Otte | Acht | Huit | Acht | Otto | Ocho |
| Extending | Udstraekkende | Uitstrekkend | Extension | Ausbreiten | Estendo | Extension |
| Extensive (or Widespread) | Udstrackt | Uitgebreid Uitgestrekt | Extendue | Verbreitet | Esteso | General |
| Falling | Faldende | Dalend, Vallend | En Baisse | Fallend | In diminuzione | En disminucion |
| Filling | Udfyldende | (Op) Vullend | Comblement | Auffüllen | Riempimento Colmamento | Relleno |
| Fine (or Fair) | Smukt, (Klart) | Mooi | Clair, Beau | Schönwetter | Sereno, bello | Sereno |
| Five | Fem | Vijf | Cinq | Fünf | Cinque | Cinco |
| Fog | Taage | Mist | Brouillard | Nebel | Nebbia | Niebla |
| Fog Bank | Taage Banke | Mist Bank | Banc de Brouillard | Nebelbank | Banco di Nebbia | Banco de Niebla |
| Forecast | Vejrforudsigelse | Verwachting | Prévision | Vorhersage | Previsione | Previsión |
| Formation | Formation | Formatie | Formation | Bildung | Formazione | Formación |
| Forming | Danne (dannende) | Vorming | Developpent, se formant | Formend, bildend | Formando | Formante |
| Four | Fire | Vier | Quatre | Vier | Quattro | Cuatro |
| Frequent | Hyppig | Veelvuldig | Fréquent | Haüfig | Frequente | Frecuenta |
| Fresh | Frisk | Fris | Fraiche, frais | Frisch | Fresco | Fresco |
| Front | Front | Front | Front | Front | Fronte | Frente |
| Front (passage of) | Front passage | Front Passage | Passage d'un Front | Frontdurch-gang | Passaggio di un Fronte | Paso de un Frente |
| Frost | Frost | Vorst | Gelée | Frost | Brina | Escarcha |
| Gale | Stormende Kuling, Hard Kuling | Stormachtig | Coup de Vent | Stürmischer wind | Burrasca | Viento Duro |
| Cones (Gale) | Oje | Kegel | Cône | Sturmekegel | Sintoma | Cona |
| Gale Warning | Stormvarsel | Stormwaarsch-uwing | Avis de coup de Vent | Sturmwarnung | Avviso di Burrasca | Aviso de Temporal |
| Good | God | Goed | Bon | Gut | Buono | Bueono |
| Gust | Vinstød, Vindkast | Windstoot | Rafale | Windstoss | Colpo di Vento, Raffica | Ráfaga, Racha |
| Gusty | Stormfuld, Byget | Buiig | (Vent) à Rafales | Böig | Con Raffiche | en Räfagas en Rachas |

| ENGLISH | DANISH | DUTCH | FRENCH | GERMAN | ITALIAN | SPANISH |
|---|---|---|---|---|---|---|
| Hail | Hagl | Hagel | Grêle | Hagel | Grandine | Granizo |
| Haze | Dis | Nevel | Brume Sèche | Dunst (Trockener) | Caligine | Calina |
| Hazy | Diset | Nevelig | Brumeux | Diesig | Caliginoso | Calinoso |
| Heavy | Svaer, Kraftig | Zwaar | Abondant, Violent | Ergiebig, Schwer | Pesante, Violento | Abunante, Violento |
| High Anticyclone | Anticyklon, Højtryk | Hogedruk- gebeid | Anticyclone | Antizyklone Hockdruck- gebiet | Anticiclone | Anticiclón |
| Hurricane | Orkan | Orkaan | Ouragan | Orkan (auuserhalb der Tropen), Hurrikan | Uragano | Huracán |
| | | | | | | |
| Increasing | Tiltagende, øgende | Toenemend | Augmentant | Zunehmend | In Auhmento | Aumentar |
| Intermittent | Intermitternde, Tiltider, Tidvis | Afwisselend | Intermittent | Zeitweilig | Intermittente | Intermitente |
| Isobar | Isobar | Isobar | Isobare | Isobare | Isobara | Isobara |
| Isolated | Isolere, Enkelte | Verspreid | Isolé | Einzeine | Isolato | Aislado |
| | | | | | | |
| Latitude | Bredde | Breedte | Latitude | Breite | Latitudine | Latitud |
| Light, slight | Tynd, let | Licht, Gering, Zwak | Faible | Schwach | Leggero, Debole | Ligero, Dehil |
| Lightning | Lyn | Bliksem | Eclair Foudre | Blitz | Lampo | Recámpago |
| Line Squall | Bygelinie | Buienlijn | Ligne de Grain | Böenfront | Linea di Groppo | Linea de Turbonada |
| Local | Lokal | Plaatselijk | Locale | Örtlich, Lokal | Locale | Local |
| Longtitude | Laengde | Lengte | Longitude | Länge | Longitudine | Longitud |
| | | | | | | |
| Meridian | Meridian | Meridiaan | Méridien | Meridian Langenkreis | Meridiano | Meridiano |
| Mist | Let Tåge, Tågedis | Nevel | Brume Légère | Dunst (Feuchter) | Foschia, Brumo | Neblina |
| Misty | Taget, Diset | Nevelig | Brumeux | Dunstig, Diesig | Brumoso, Fosco | Brumoso |
| Moderate | Middlemadig, Moderat | Matig, Gematigd | Modéré | Mässig | Moderato | Moderado |
| Moderating | Beherske | Matigend, Afnemend | Se Modérant Se Calmant | Abschwäch- end Abnehmend | Medianente, Calmante | Medianente |
| Morning (in the) | Om Formiddagen Om Morgenen | Morgen, Voormiddag | Le Matin | Morgens | Al Mattino, Par il Mattino | Por la Manana |
| Moving | Bevaegende | Bewegend | Se Déplaçant | Ziehend | In Movimento, Si Muove | Movimiento |

| ENGLISH | DANISH | DUTCH | FRENCH | GERMAN | ITALIAN | SPANISH |
|---|---|---|---|---|---|---|
| Nine | Ni | Negen | Neuf | Neun | Nove | Nueve |
| North | Nord | Noorden | Nord | Nord | Settentionale, Nord | Septentrional, Boreal |
| | | | | | | |
| Occasional | Af og til, Ti tider | At en toe | Eparses | Teilweise | Occasionale | Occasional |
| Occlusion | Okklusion | Okklusie | Occlusion | Okklusion | Occlusion | Oclusion |
| Off-shore Wind | Fra land vind | Aflandige wind | Vent de Terre | Ablandiger Wind, Landwind | Vento (Brezza) di Terra | Viento Terral |
| One | Een | Een | Un(e) | Eins | Uno | Uno |
| On-shore Wind | I land vind Palånsvind | Wind van zee | Vent de mer Brise de mer | Auflandiger Wind, Seewind | Vento (Brezza) di mare | Viento de mar |
| Overcast | Overtrukket Overskyet | Geheel bewolkt | Couvert | Bedeckt | Coperto | Cubierto |
| | | | | | | |
| Period | Periode | Tijdvak, Periode | Période | Periode | Periodo | Periodo |
| Period of Validity | Glydigheds- periode | Geldigheids- duur | Période de Validité | Gültigkeis- dauer | Periodo di Validità | Periodo de Validez |
| Poor | Ringe, Sigt | Gering Slecht | Mauvais | Schlecht | Mao, Scarso | Mal |
| Precipitation | Nedbør | Neerslag | Précipitation | Niederschlag | Precipitazione | Precipitación |
| Pressure | Tryk | Druk | Pression | Druck | Pressione | Presión |
| | | | | | | |
| Quickly | Kvick, Hurtigt | Zeer Snel | Rapidement | Schnell | Pronto | Pronto |
| | | | | | | |
| Rain | Regn | Regen | Pluie | Regen | Pioggia | Pluvial, Lluvia |
| Continuous (rain) | Uafbrudt redvarende | Onafgebroken | Continue | Anhaltend | Continua | Continuo |
| Slight (rain) | Let | Licht, Gering | Faible | Leicht | Pioggia debole | Débil Legero |
| Ridge | Ryg | Rug | Dorsale | Rücken | Promontorio | Dorsal |
| Rising | Stigning | Rijzend, Stijgend | En Hausse | Steigend | Ascendente | Ascendente |
| Rough | Oprørt | Guur | Agitée | Stürmisch | Agitato, Grosso | Bravo o alborotado |
| | | | | | | |
| Scattered | Spredt, Stro | Verspreide | Sporadiques | Zerstreut | Diffuso | Difuso |
| Sea | Sø, Hav | Zee | Mer | Meer | Mare | Mar |
| Sea Breeze | Søbrise, Havbris | Zeewind | Brise de Mer | Seebrise | Brezze di mare | Virazón |
| Seven | Syv | Zeven | Sept | Sieben | Sette | Siete |

| ENGLISH | DANISH | DUTCH | FRENCH | GERMAN | ITALIAN | SPANISH |
|---|---|---|---|---|---|---|
| Shower | Byge | Regenbui | Averse | Regenschauer | Rovescio | Aguavero, Chubasco |
| Six | Seks | Zes | Six | Sechs | Sei | Seis |
| Sleet | Slud, sne og regne | Natte sneeuw | Grésil | Schneeregen | Nevischio | Aguanieve |
| Slowly | Langsomt | Zie Langzaam | Lentement | Langsam | Lentamente | Lentamente |
| Smooth | Glatte | Vlak | Belle | Glatt | Tranquillo, Calmo | Tranquilo, Calmo |
| Snow | Sne | Sneeuw | Neige | Schnee | Neve | Neive |
| South | Syd | Zuiden | Sud | Süd | Meridionale | Sur |
| Squall | Byge | Windvlaag | Grain | Böe | Tempestra | Turbonada |
| State of Sea | Sø Stat, Søeus Tilstand | Toestand van de zee | État de la mer | Zustand der See | Stato del mare | Estado del mare |
| Stationary | Stationaer | Stationair | Stationnaire | Stationär | Stazionario | Estacionario |
| Steadily | Regelmaessig | Geregeld, Regelmatig | Regulièrement | Regelmässig | Constante- mente | Constante- mente |
| Storm | Uneir | Storm | Tempête | Sturm | Tempesta, Tembrale | Temporal |
| Strong | Staerk, Kraftig | Sterk, Krachtig | Fort | Stark | Forte | Fuerte |
| Swell | Dønning | Deining | Houle | Dünung | Onda lunga, Mare lungo | Martendida, Mar de Leva |
| | | | | | | |
| Ten | Ti | Tien | Dix | Zehn | Dieci | Diez |
| Three | Tre | Drie | Trois | Drei | Tre | Tres |
| Thunder | Torden | Donder | Tonnerre | Donner | Tuono | Tormenta |
| Thunderstorm | Tordenvejr | Onweer | Orage | Gewitter | Temporale | Trueno |
| Time | Tid | Tijd | Temps | Zeit | Tempo | Hora |
| Trough | Udlober, Trug | Trog | Creux | Trog | Saccatura | Vaguada |
| Two | To | Twee | Deux | Zwei | Due | Duo |
| | | | | | | |
| Variable | Foranderlig Variabel | Veranderliik | Variable | Veränderlich | Variabile | Variable |
| Veering | Drejer til Højre | Ruimend | Virement ou Virage | Rechtdrehend, Ausschiessen | Rotazione ovaria, Rotazione a destra | Dextrogiro |
| Visibility | Sigt, Sigtbarhed | Zicht | Visibilité | Sicht | Visibilitá | Visibilidad |
| | | | | | | |
| Warm | Varm | Warm | Chaud | Warm | Cáldo | Cálido |
| Waterspout | Skypumpe | Waterhoos | Trombe Marine | Wasserhose | Tromba Marina | Tromba Marina |
| Wave formation | Bølgeformation | Golfformatie | Formation des Vagues | Wellenbildung | Formazione di onde | Formación de ondas |
| Weather | Vejr | Weer | Temps | Wetter | Tempo | Tiempo |
| Weather Conditions | Vejr-Betingelse | Weer- somstandig- heden | Conditions du Temps | Wetter- Verhältnisse | Condizioni del Tempo | Condiciones del Tiempo |

| ENGLISH | DANISH | DUTCH | FRENCH | GERMAN | ITALIAN | SPANISH |
|---------|--------|-------|--------|--------|---------|---------|
| Weather Report | Vejrmelding | Weerbericht | Rapport, Bulletin Météorologique | Wettermeldung Wetterboricht | Rapporto, (Bolletino) Meteoroligico | Informe, aviso Boletin, Meteorologico |
| West | Vest | Westen | Ouest | West | Ovest, Ponente | Oeste |
| Whirlwind | Hvirvelvind | Windhoos | Tourbillon de Vent | Wirbelwind | Turbine | Torbellino |
| Wind | Vind | Wind | Vent | Wind | Vento | Viento |
| Wind Force | Vindstyrke | Windkracht | Force du Vent | Windstärke | Forza (Intensita) del Vento | Intensidad Fuerrza del Viento |

## NUMBERS

| | | | | | | |
|---------|--------|-------|--------|--------|---------|---------|
| One | Een | Een | Un(e) | Eins | Uno | Uno |
| Two | To | Twee | Deux | Zwei | Due | Duo |
| Three | Tre | Drie | Trois | Drei | Tre | Tres |
| Four | Fire | Vier | Quatre | Vier | Quattro | Cuatro |
| Five | Fem | Vijf | Cinq | Fünf | Cinque | Cinco |
| Six | Seks | Zes | Six | Sechs | Sei | Seis |
| Seven | Syv | Zeven | Sept | Sieben | Sette | Siete |
| Eight | Otte | Acht | Huit | Acht | Otto | Ocho |
| Nine | Ni | Negen | Neuf | Neun | Nove | Nueve |
| Ten | Ti | Tien | Dix | Zehn | Dieci | Diez |